Magic Moments™
Exploring Nature With Your Kids

Written by Patricia A. Staino
Illustrated by Marilynn G. Barr

The Education Center, Inc.
Greensboro, North Carolina

For all the backyards in the Bronx

©1997 by THE EDUCATION CENTER, INC.
All rights reserved except as noted below.

Library of Congress Cataloging-in-Publication Data

Staino, Patricia A., 1970–
    Exploring nature with your kids / written by Patricia A. Staino ;
illustrated by Marilynn G. Barr.
        p.   cm. — (Magic moments)
    Includes index.
    Summary: Over one hundred nature activities for children to do with their parents,
covering such topics as outdoor games, leaves, greenhouses, and weather.
    ISBN 1-56234-193-6 (pbk.)
    1. Nature study—Activity programs—Juvenile literature.
2. Nature craft—Juvenile literature. [1. Nature study.
2. Handicraft.] I. Barr, Marilynn G., ill. II. Title.
III. Series: Magic moments (Greensboro, N.C.)
QH54.5.S735   1997
508—dc21   97-42039
                                                                  CIP
                                                                  AC

Cover illustration by Marilynn Grant Barr

The Education Center, Inc.
P.O. Box 9753
Greensboro, NC 27429-0753

Manufactured in the United States
10 9 8 7 6 5 4 3 2 1 0

EXPLORING NATURE

WITH YOUR KIDS

My Nature Scrapbook by Colleen

Table of Contents

Table of Contents

Dear Kids,

If you like to play outside, you'll love this book! It's filled with games, toys, experiments, and projects for the great outdoors!

There are lots of activities for all kinds of neighborhoods and all kinds of weather. If you live in the city, you can try The Sidewalk Game or make In-Town Rubbings. If you live in the country, you can plant a vegetable garden or build a greenhouse. You can do most of the activities no matter where you live! There are even activities for bringing nature into your own house.

You may think that exploring nature means running around looking for insects with a magnifying lens. But learning about nature can mean blowing bubbles or painting in the snow. It might mean building an igloo or planting tomatoes. Or maybe it's feeding the birds or making a map of your neighborhood. You learn and understand more about nature no matter what you are doing while you are outside.

Playing outdoors is a great way to spend time with your family. Try some of these activities on your next vacation or on a lazy Sunday afternoon. Choose a fun project, dress for outdoors, and you're on your way....

Dear Mom & Dad,

Do your kids love being outside so much that you have to drag them in for dinner? Or are you always trying to push them outside when they would rather be watching TV? No matter what your kids are like, this book will make outdoor playtime a fun time for your family. These games and projects give nature lovers new ideas and challenges. They will even tempt the couch potatoes to step outside!

All the projects focus on observing, reading and following directions, and using good sense. Each project is rated for the level of ease. On page 8, you can read what each rating means. The ratings are based on the necessary skills as well as the number of different skills used in a single project. Some activities were also rated higher because an adult should be present. Kids can hike or play on a water slide by themselves, but it's usually a good idea to have some adult supervision.

If your child is eager to try a project that you think may be rated a little high for her, try it anyway. If she is interested and you are there to help, no project is too hard. On the other hand, if your child seems bored by an activity, try something else. These projects are meant to be fun, not work.

This book is great for a family vacation, a day at Grandma's, or a weekend afternoon at home. Whether you live in the city, the suburbs, or the country, you are sure to find the right games to make magic moments outdoors with your kids!

About This Book

Ladybug Ratings

At the top of each project page you will find one to four ladybugs. They show you how easy or hard a project is. Here's what they mean:

 The instructions are easy. These projects can be done without an adult.

 The projects require cutting with a knife or scissors, or using the stove. The directions are still fairly easy. An adult should help.

 Projects may be a little more advanced. You may have to go outside your own backyard. They also may ask you to use a knife or the stove. An adult should help.

 There are lots of steps or some of the steps are hard. Also, you may have to walk around your neighborhood or be away from home for awhile. You definitely need an adult to help.

The Pocket Watches

 A pocket watch inside the materials box means that these projects take a little time to finish. A project may need to dry overnight or grow for a few weeks. Be sure you have enough time to complete the project.

Stop Signs

 This symbol means that the next step is more difficult. You may have to use an iron, an oven, or a knife. Ask a grown-up to help you whenever you see a stop sign.

The Nature Notes Pages

These pages give you a little extra information about nature. They will explain how certain things work or why things happen. At the bottom of these pages are boxes with fun ideas to try.

The Great Outdoors

What do you do when you play outside? Do you ride your bike? Play soccer? Skate? You can have a lot of fun when you take time to play with nature! Use the things you see around you in your games. Or just do something out-side where you can enjoy the fresh air—blow bubbles, eat a snack, or take a walk.

Find a Secret Hideout

The outdoors is a great place to spend some time alone reading, thinking, and dreaming.

A tepee

Tie four old broomsticks together at one end. Spread the other ends apart, and stick them into the ground. Cover the sticks with an old sheet.

A box house

Take a bunch of appliance boxes and tape them together. With a grown-up's help, cut out windows and doors.

A hedge

The simplest hideaway! Find a tall hedge, spread out a blanket behind it, and relax.

A table tent

Throw an old sheet over a card table.

SMITH FAMILY HIDEOUT

Build a Sand Castle

Experiment with these ideas and come up with your own unique sand castle.

You'll need:
small shovel
plastic spoons
different-size paper cups
sticks, stones, and shells for decorations

1. Start by smoothing out the sand where you want to build the castle.

2. Be sure to mix a little water with the sand you are going to use for building. This will help it hold together.

3. Begin the castle by piling up lots of sand to make the main building. Use your hands and shovel to pat it smooth and shape it the way you want.

4. Add towers and turrets to your castle. Use the paper cups to make these forms. Carefully place the filled cups upside down on the main building. Tap on the cup bottoms to make the forms slide out.

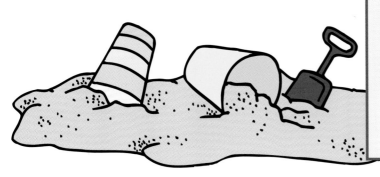

5. Use the plastic spoons to carve windows and doors and other decorations on the castle. Add the stones, sticks, and shells as decorations.

How big can you make your sand castle? Some people work hard at making really big castles. Using just hands, shovels, and buckets, a group in British Columbia, Canada, created a castle in 1993 that was over 21 feet high! And teachers and students of Ellon Academy near Aberdeen, Scotland, used even more sand in 1988 when they built a castle that was more than five miles long!

Build a City

Practice being an architect! You can build your stone city inside or outside, but you can find your building materials only in the great outdoors.

You'll need:

lots of different-sized rocks (be sure
    they are washed and dried)
glue
small sticks
sand
paints
paintbrushes
top from a large gift box
paper
small mirror

1. Place the box top flat side down wherever you want to build your city. Pour enough sand into the box to cover the bottom.

2. Use your fingers to draw streets in the sand. You can line the streets with small pebbles.

3. Glue together rocks and twigs to make houses and skyscrapers. Use stacks of flat rocks to make apartment buildings and glue small stones together to make walls for houses. Use paper to make roofs and chimneys. Paint on windows and doors.

4. Put a park in your city. Use the sticks to make trees, swing sets, and park benches.

Lay a small mirror on the ground to make a lake. Glue and paint rocks to look like flowers and gardens.

5. Glue together rocks to make small people. Paint them and let them dry.

6. When everything has dried, you can play with your city and its people.

The oldest capital city in the world is Damascus, Syria. There have been people living there continuously for almost 4,500 years!

Throw a Block Party

These neighborhood street parties are really popular in cities during the summer.

You'll need:

paper
markers and crayons
friendly neighbors
food and game equipment from your
    friendly neighbors
poster board

1. STOP Ask a grown-up to help you plan your block party. Together decide on a good day and time to hold it. Also, ask your helper to get permission from the local police department to get the street closed off to traffic. If you can't get the street closed off, try to find a big backyard or an empty lot.

2. Make invitations. Be sure they say where and when the block party will be. Ask everybody to bring some kind of food for the food table and to bring their own drinks. Ask them to call you and let you know if they will be there. Be sure to pick a *rain date* in case the weather is bad. Put one invitation in each neighbor's mailbox two weeks before the party. You can also make a few signs to put outside to announce the event.

Block Party
When:
Where:
Please come!

3. Decide what games you will play at the block party. Try tug-of-war, red rover, balloon toss, volleyball, and soccer. Decide what contests you want to have, like pie-eating or pie-throwing, watermelon-eating, egg toss, and others. Decide what equipment you need. Ask neighbors to bring some of the equipment or be in charge of the events.

4. Decide what time each game and contest will be. Write the names of the games and the times they will be played on a piece of poster board.

5. On the day of the party, ask some grown-ups to block off the street. Set up a table for the food. Hang up the poster board schedule. Now get ready to have some fun!

Schedule

9:00 Pie-Throwing
10:00 Face Painting
11:00 Square Dancing
12:00 Acrobats
1:00 Sack Race

The largest party ever held was a kind of block party. On May 30–31, 1979, a party was held in Hyde Park in London, England, to celebrate the International Year of the Child. About 160,000 children came to the party.

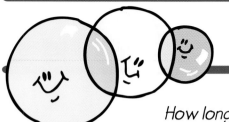

Bubble Fun

How long will your bubbles float without popping?

Bottle Blower

You'll need:

bubble mixture
small plastic soda bottle
scissors

1. 🛑 Ask a grown-up to cut off the top third of the bottle.

2. Take the cap off the bottle top.

3. To blow bubbles, dip the cut end of the bottle into the bubble mixture. Blow through the mouth of the bottle.

Bubble Pipe

You'll need:

bubble mixture
scissors
pointed-bottom paper cup
pushpin
pencil
flexible plastic straw

1. 🛑 Cut off the bottom 1½ inches from the paper cup. You can throw the top part away.

2. Make a hole with the pushpin about ½ inch up from the point.

3. Push the pencil point through the pushpin hole until the hole is big enough for the straw to fit through snugly.

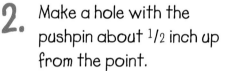

4. Push the short end of the straw into the hole.

5. Pour a little of the bubble mixture into the pipe. Blow into the straw to make bubbles.

Bubble Mixture

You'll need:
6 ounces water
2 ounces dishwashing detergent
5 drops glycerin
eyedropper
jar

1. Pour the water into the jar.

2. Add the dishwashing detergent.

3. Add the glycerin.

4. Stir the mixture well. To use, pour the bubble mixture into a bowl. When you are finished playing, pour what is left of the bubble mixture into the jar and cover it with a lid.

In 1988 a man named David Stein blew a bubble that was 50 feet long! All he used was a bubble wand, dishwashing liquid, and water.

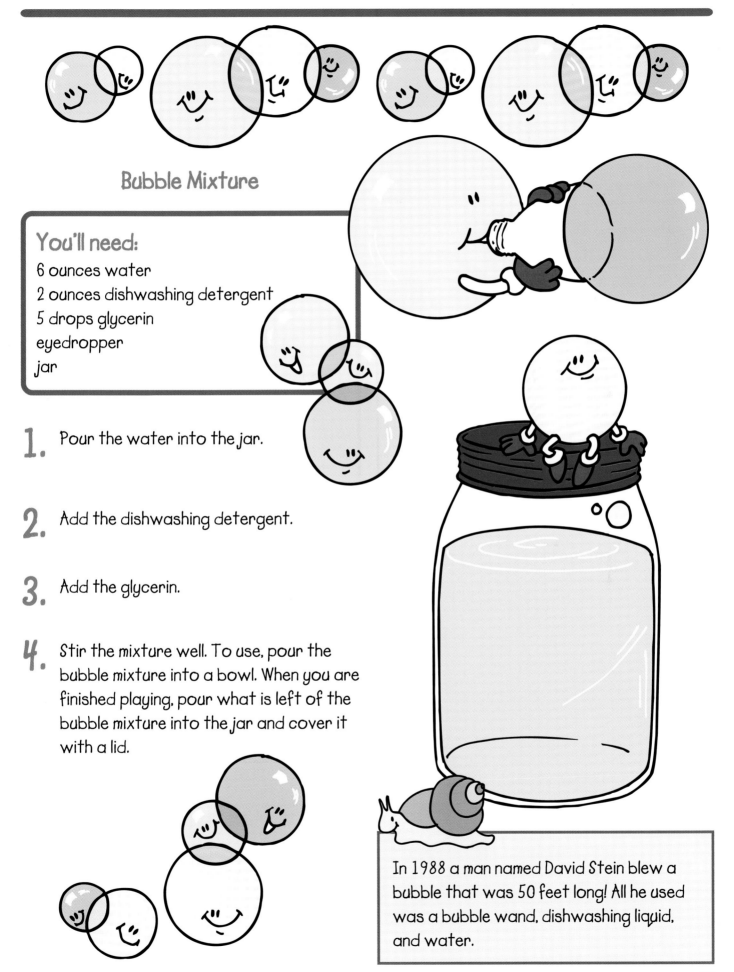

Take a Hike

Try exploring nature while getting a little exercise.

You'll need:

comfortable shoes
backpack
snacks
flashlight
sunscreen
bug repellent
compass
extra socks
first-aid supplies
water to drink

1. Pack all your gear in the backpack—except your shoes! You should be wearing those! You have enough equipment for a short hike in an area that is near other people (in a park, for example). If you want to go on a longer hike farther away, you will need other equipment like a change of clothes, a rain jacket, matches, whistle, food, stuff to cook with, a knife, rope, sleeping bag, and toilet paper. But start out slow on a short hike and leave the all-day hiking for later.

2. Decide where you will hike. STOP Be sure a grown-up is going with you.

3. When you are hiking, follow these rules:

- Stay on the trail. Stay with your grown-up.
- Eat and drink as you go. Stop and rest when you are tired.
- Leave the trail the way you found it. Don't litter. Don't pick flowers and plants.
- Never eat any berries or other plants you find on the trail.

Water Slide

It's like having a water park in your own backyard!

You'll need:
large piece of heavy plastic
4 heavy rocks or bricks
hose with a sprinkler attached

1. Clear a grassy area where there are no rocks, trees, or other objects in the way.

2. Lay the plastic on the ground with one rock on each corner.

3. Set up the sprinkler next to the plastic. When the sprinkler is turned on, the water should spray onto the plastic.

4. Wear your bathing suit. When the plastic is wet, start sliding and flopping onto the plastic. Leave the sprinkler on the whole time.

5. After 30 minutes, move the sprinkler and the plastic. It's not good for the grass to get too much water.

Nature Notes: Finding Nature in the City

You may think you can't enjoy nature if you live in a city. But that's not true. There are many natural things to see and do when you step outside your home. You may not have vast fields or dirt roads. You may not be able to see a lot of clouds or stars because of the tall buildings. But doesn't that make spending time in a quiet park in the middle of your city even more wonderful?

If you live in a city, you can see how nature survives in places where man has taken over. Notice where birds make nests when there aren't many trees. Look for stray plants and flowers popping up in cracks in the sidewalk. Where do the squirrels look for nuts and food to save for the winter?

Cities and towns have animals and plants just like the country does. Spend time in your local park. What kinds of birds and flowers do you see there? Are they different from the birds and flowers you find on the street?

You can organize special projects to help nature survive in your city. Get your neighbors together for a Clean-Up Day on your block. Pick up trash and sweep the sidewalks. Maybe you can find a little plot of soil and plant some flowers.

It may not be easy to find nature in the city, but it is there and it is definitely worth looking for.

Try this:
- With a grown-up's help, place a dish of bird food on the fire escape. Watch the different kinds of birds that stop by for a snack.
- Plant some flowers in flowerpots and set them outside on your stoop or windowsill.
- Start a Nature Notebook! Record what kinds of plants and animals you see in your local park on a summer's day. Go back in the winter and see if they are still there.

Summer Snowball Fight

Here's a frosty way to cool off in the summer.

2 or more players

You'll need:

snow
zippered plastic bags

1. During the winter, make a bunch of snowballs. Place the snowballs in a plastic bag. Tell your friends to do the same.

2. If a grown-up says it's okay, keep the snowballs in the freezer until summer.

3. On a hot summer day, call up your friends and tell them to take their bag of snowballs out of the freezer and meet you outside. Let the snowballs defrost for a few minutes.

4. Then take the snowballs outside, and let the fun begin!

Winter Picnic

Picnic baskets are not just for warm and sunny days.

You'll need:

Thermos® jugs
spoons
napkins
food
big bag or basket
old plastic tablecloth

1. Make peanut butter and jelly sandwiches. Wrap up some cookies, muffins, cheese, and crackers. Put hot soup and hot chocolate in the Thermos® jugs. Place everything in a big bag or basket.

2. Be sure you dress warmly enough for the weather.

3. Go outside and find a place to have your picnic. Spread the plastic tablecloth on the ground and sit on top of it.

4. Enjoy! Be sure to pick up all trash and put away leftover food.

Nature Notes: Snow

You may like to play in the snow. Or maybe you live someplace where it is still warm enough to go swimming in the winter. Did you ever wonder why it snows in one place and not in another?

Snow is made when the air up in the clouds gets below freezing. It needs to be cold for snow to fall. That's why places like Florida have very little snowfall. It is usually too warm in southern states for snow to form.

Clouds are made up of tiny droplets of water. The water droplets evaporated from lakes, oceans, and streams and were carried upward into the air. Eventually, these droplets will fall to the earth again as rain.

When the air in a cloud goes below the freezing point, the water droplets become tiny ice crystals. The ice crystals start joining together. They form patterns that look like snowflakes. Eventually, these ice crystals will be released from the clouds as snow.

Snowflakes can be very tiny. Sometimes as many as 100 crystals join together to make a snowflake that is more than an inch wide.

Snow does not contain as much water as rain does. One inch of rain is the same as six inches of moist snow and 30 inches of dry, fluffy snow!

Snowflakes don't last very long. If you catch one on your mitten, it will melt away very quickly. One scientist found a way to catch snowflakes and keep them cold long enough to take pictures of them. He was called "Snowflake" Bentley. He took more than a thousand pictures of snowflakes. Every single snowflake he photographed was different.

In 1936 a Japanese scientist created artificial snow in his laboratory. Later, some American scientists made fake snow outdoors. They added artificial ice particles to very cold clouds. Today, there are machines that can make artificial snow for ski trails.

Try this:
- Try to think of a way to catch snowflakes and keep them cold so you can compare their patterns.
- If you live in a place that gets snow, record how many inches of snow you get this winter. Figure out how many inches of rain that would be.
- If you go skiing, find out if the ski resort makes artificial snow. Look at it. Does it look and feel just like real snow?

Build an Igloo

We think of an igloo as a snow house built by the Inuit people.
But their word "igloo" means any kind of house.
Today snow houses are used only as temporary shelters for hunters and fishermen.

You'll need:

loaf pan
wet snow

2. Continue piling bricks on top of each other. Overlap them, as shown below.

1. Make snow bricks with your loaf pan. Pack the wet snow in well. Turn the loaf pan upside down to slide the brick into place. Lay the bricks in a circle, pressing them against each other. Leave an opening in the circle for a door.

3. As you get closer to the top, move the bricks inward to make a dome.

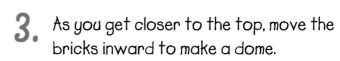

Snow Trivia

- One single snowstorm dumped 189 inches of snow at Mount Shasta Ski Bowl, California, from February 13 to February 19, 1959.
- On February 7, 1963, 78 inches of snow fell on Mile 47 Camp, Cooper River Division, Alaska, in 24 hours. That's the most snow that's ever fallen in one day!
- The most snow to fall in a one-year period fell on Paradise, Mount Rainier, Washington. A total of 1,224 1/2 inches fell between February 19, 1971 and February 18, 1972.
- The most snow on the ground was 37 feet 7 inches in Tamarac, California, in March 1911.

Snow Painting

*Your masterpiece won't last forever,
but you'll have a great time creating it.*

You'll need:
squeeze bottles
food coloring

1. Fill the bottles with water. Add food coloring until you have the color you want.

2. Go outside and find a pile of snow.

3. Paint pictures, write your name, or make designs in the snow with the colored water.

Fun & Games

Playing outside is the best! There is no better way to enjoy nature than to be right in the middle of it. With just your imagination, you can think of lots of fun games to play.

Many outside games have been around for a long time—Mom and Dad probably still remember some of their favorites! Ask them what games they played when they were your age.

When you play outside, you have lots of room, so you can really spread out. It's okay if you laugh really loud and make a little noise. And you don't have to worry about knocking things over or messing up the house. On the next sunny day, take your whole family out for some good old-fashioned fun!

London

This game is a little like hopscotch and a little like Hangman!

2 to 6 players

You'll need:

chalk
bottle caps

1. Draw a large rectangle, about three feet by five feet, on a sidewalk or paved driveway. Add lines and a curved top so it looks like this drawing. Write the word "LONDON" in the curved section.

2. Players take turns throwing bottle caps. The first player stands at the straight end of the playing board. She throws her bottle cap. If the cap lands in one of the rectangular sections, she draws a small circle in that section and writes her initials inside. This little circle is a head.

3. The first player throws again. If the cap lands in the same section, she draws a body under the head. If it lands in a different section, she draws another little head and initials it.

4. The first player throws until her bottle cap lands on the line between two spaces or outside the playing board. She keeps adding to the bodies she has started until each has a head, a body, and two legs (draw only one leg per turn). If she finishes drawing a body in one section and her cap lands there again, she starts drawing a new head.

5. If her cap lands on the London space, she can draw one body part in every rectangular section.

6. When a player has drawn three complete bodies in one section, she draws a line through all three bodies. Now she owns that section. If another player throws his bottle cap in that section, he loses a turn.

7. The game is over when all the sections are owned. The player who owns the most sections is the winner.

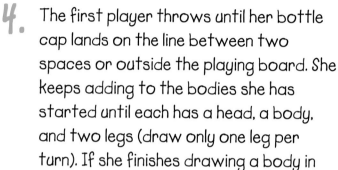

Bowls

When King George III of England outlawed indoor games, this half-ball game became a popular outdoor sport.

2 to 5 players

You'll need:

round, foam ball (like a Nerf® ball), cut in half

15 empty soda cans

1. On a sidewalk or other hard ground, make a wide circle out of the soda cans. The cans should be standing up. They should also be evenly spaced.

2. Players take turns bowling. Stand about ten feet from the circle. To bowl, hold the ball in your hand so that the flat side is facing out. Roll the ball so that it slides out of your hand and moves to either the left or the right of the circle. (This could take some practice!)

3. Players get one point for each can they knock over. In every round each player gets two turns, one after the other. After a player's second turn, all the cans are set up again so they are standing.

4. If you throw the ball so it shoots out in front and hits the cans that are right in front of you, you lose your turn and don't get any points for that round.

5. The first player to get 25 points wins the game.

To make the game harder: Make the circle even wider, stand 20 feet away, or raise the winning score to 50.

Bowling

Who needs a bowling alley?
Now you can play in the great outdoors!

2 or more players

You'll need:

flat concrete area or sidewalk
10 empty 2-liter soda bottles
large ball (about the size of a
   soccer ball)
masking tape
pencil
paper

1. Set up the bottles in a triangular shape as shown (four bottles in back, three bottles in front of the four, two bottles in front of the three, and one bottle in front of them all).

2. About ten feet away from the bottles, place a piece of masking tape on the ground.

3. In every round each player gets two turns, one right after the other. Standing behind the line, a player rolls the ball toward the bottles. If the player knocks any bottles down on the first roll, do not pick them up. After the second roll, be sure all the bottles are standing before the next person rolls the ball.

4. A player gets one point for each bottle he knocks down. If a player knocks down all the bottles in his first turn of the round, he gets an extra 15 points (25 points total). If he knocks down all the bottles in two turns, he gets a ten-point bonus (20 points total).

5. There are ten rounds in each game. The winner is the player with the most points at the end of ten rounds.

If you bowl a perfect game in bowling, you get 300 points. That means you have to knock down all the pins on EVERY turn. It's hard to do, but kids have done it. Scott Owsley of California, 10 years old, did it. So did 12-year-old Nicole Long of Missouri. But bowling is for people of every age! In 1992, an 81-year-old man from Florida bowled a perfect game. He was the oldest person to ever hit 300!

Backyard Miniature Golf

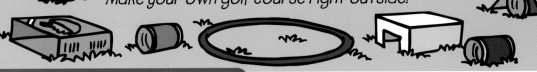

Make your own golf course right outside!

2 or more players

You'll need:

child-size golf club, or a yardstick and
    a new sponge, for each player
masking tape
markers
golf ball
9 clean and empty soup cans
materials to use to make the obstacles:
    boxes, paper plates, scissors,
    glue, tape, cans, and other objects

1. To make your own golf club, use the masking tape to attach the sponge to the end of a yardstick.

2. Decide where you want to put the holes. At each point lay a can on its side. Be sure there is enough space around each hole.

3. At each hole build a small obstacle that players must get the ball around.

4. Place a piece of masking tape on each can. On the tape, write the number of the hole.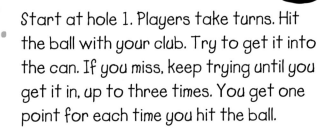

5. Start at hole 1. Players take turns. Hit the ball with your club. Try to get it into the can. If you miss, keep trying until you get it in, up to three times. You get one point for each time you hit the ball.

6. Write down how many tries it takes each player to put the ball in the can. The winner is the person with the least amount of points at the end of nine holes.

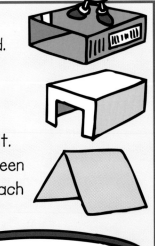

Obstacle Ideas:

- Lay an empty cereal box down. Keep one end open and one end closed.
- Cut little doors in the small ends of a shoebox. Lay the box, open side down, in front of the hole.
- Fold a piece of cardboard in half. Stand it in front of the hole so it makes a little tent. Add two or three of these to make it really difficult.
- Make walls on the side of the fairway. The fairway is the space between where you hit the ball and where the hole is. Put a row of blocks on each side. To make it interesting, make the row zigzag back and forth.
- Lay a Hula-Hoop® somewhere on the course.

What other obstacles can you think of?

Tug-of-War

Play this game with your family, your friends, or your whole neighborhood!

2 or more players

You'll need:

long, thick rope
short length of rope

1. Find a grassy or sandy area where you can play. Divide into two teams. If it's your family, try the kids against the adults or mix it up!

2. Lay the small piece of rope on the ground. The teams line up on opposite sides of the short rope. All the players hold onto the longer rope with both hands.

3. Someone yells, "Go!" Both teams pull the rope toward their side. A team wins when the first player on the other team steps over the piece of rope that is on the ground.

Some people take tug-of-war very seriously. Some compete in tournaments. There is even a World Championship of tug-of-war. England has won that competition more times than any other country.

Your tugs-of-war may not last very long, but some teams just don't lose their grip! In 1889, English soldiers in India had a tug-of-war that lasted 2 hours, 41 minutes!

Nature Safari

You can make every scavenger hunt different just by changing the list.

2 or more players

You'll need:

pencils
paper
plastic bags

1. Make a list of things to look for on the hunt. Here are some ideas:

   pine needles
   pinecones
   yellow flower
   an ant
   butterfly
   mushroom
   STOP (Do NOT eat—some are poisonous!)
   three different kinds of leaves
   white rock
   smooth rock
   red flower
   moss
   something that floats
   berries in season
   STOP (Do NOT eat—save for the birds.)

2. Give each player a list of things to find and a plastic bag. Choose a place to be home base. Now try to find everything on your list.

3. The first person to find everything on the list (or the most items after a given time) and return to home base is the winner. The winner should call everyone back to home base. Each player should show the others the objects she found.

Other ways to play:

- If you don't want to take living things from their natural homes, don't put them in a bag. Just check them off on your list. Be honest!

- Set a time limit for your game. Decide how long you want to hunt. Ask someone with a watch to call you back to home base when time is up. The player who found the most items is the winner.

Wacky Water-Balloon Toss

Try this on a hot summer day—it just may cool you and your buddy off! Count on getting wet!

You'll need:

2 players

balloons
water

1. With help, fill a balloon with water and tie it shut.

2. Players stand outside facing each other. One player tosses the balloon to the other. The other player catches it—hopefully!

3. After the balloon is caught, both players take a step backward.

4. Continue tossing the balloon until someone misses and the balloon breaks. The winner is the player who tossed the balloon to the player who dropped it.

Another way to play:

Both players hold a water balloon. They count to three and toss the balloons to each other at the same time. When they both catch the balloons, they both take a step backward. If a player drops a balloon and it breaks, the other player wins.

33

Nature Notes: Sidewalk Games

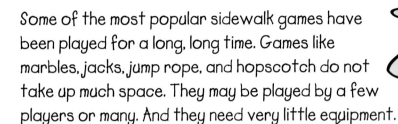

Some of the most popular sidewalk games have been played for a long, long time. Games like marbles, jacks, jump rope, and hopscotch do not take up much space. They may be played by a few players or many. And they need very little equipment.

Jacks is played with a small rubber ball and little metal or plastic objects called *jacks*. Usually the jacks are tossed on the ground. In the basic game, you then toss the ball in the air, let it bounce once, and grab a certain number of jacks. You must catch the ball before it bounces a second time.

There are many different jacks games. Playing jacks goes back as far as ancient Greek and Roman times. It is still played all over the world. You can use stones, beans, kernels of corn, or seeds in place of regular metal jacks.

Hopscotch is a hopping game played on a board drawn on or etched into the ground. Hopscotch is played all over the world, and there is no one gameboard or one way to play. The board is made up of rectangles and squares. Players take turns tossing markers onto the board and hopping around the squares. They might hop in a certain order. They might have to kick the marker to different squares or pick up the marker while hopping.

Marbles is a game played with small, hard balls. Marbles are usually about ¹/₂ inch to an inch around. They are usually made of glass and are very pretty to look at. Marbles games need to be played on a flat, level surface. For most games you must shoot marbles. That means you hold a large marble be-tween your thumb and pointer finger. Use your thumb to shoot the marble at another marble to hit it. You must keep at least one knuckle on the ground when you shoot.

There are many different ways to play marbles. This game has been around a long time. Roman Emperor Augustus Caesar played *Nuces*, a form of marbles that used round nuts, when he was a little boy. And small marbles made of baked clay were found in prehistoric caves.

Jump rope has been around for a *loooooong* time, be-cause rope has been around for thousands of years. You can jump rope by yourself or play with at least two other people. You can try running through the rope or skipping on one foot or jumping really, really fast. There are many songs and chants that people sing while jumping rope, and they've been around for a long time, too.

Try this:
- Ask a grown-up to teach you how to play marbles, jacks, or hopscotch.
- Collect a bunch of flat stones to use as jacks. Make up your own jacks games.
- Make up your own jump-rope rhyme.
- Practice shooting a marble.

The Sidewalk Game

You and your family become life-size game pieces in this game.

2 or more players

You'll need:

chalk
dice

2. To play, roll the dice. Move the number of spaces you roll. Stand on that space. Do what the square says.

3. The winner is the first person to reach the FINISH square.

1. Find a stretch of sidewalk (15 or 20 squares). Use the chalk to make each square part of a gameboard. Write START on the first square. Write FINISH on the last square. In between, you can write all kinds of fun directions like these:

Go back to Start.
Move ahead two spaces.
Hop on one foot and count to ten.
Free turn.
Go back three spaces.
Switch spots with the player behind you.
Sing a song.

Up & Away

It's really fun to make toy flying machines. You can race them. You can make them do fancy tricks. You can put on an air show for your family and friends.

The best place to fly your toys is outdoors. With a little help from the wind, they'll go even farther than *you* would have imagined!

Paper Airplane

Make a paper airplane that will soar.

You'll need:

8$\frac{1}{2}$-inch by 11-inch piece of paper
ruler
scissors
pencil

1. Fold the paper in half. Open it up and lay it flat on the table.

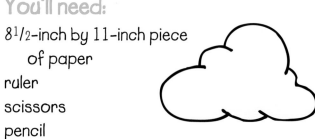

2. Fold one of the long sides down to make a $\frac{1}{4}$-inch flap. Fold that flap over about 10 more times, until the paper is 4$\frac{1}{2}$ inches by 11 inches.

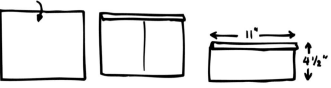

3. Fold the paper in half again.

4. Draw a line like the one shown here. 🛑 Cut along that line.

5. Unfold the plane. Fold the wing tips toward the center as shown.

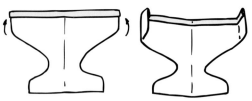

6. Turn the plane upside down. Fold the tips of the tail toward the center.

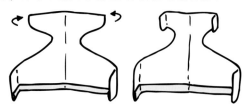

7. To fly the plane, stand on a chair. (This plane flies best if it starts from a high place.) Hold the plane so that the crease is between your fingertips. Throw it gently.

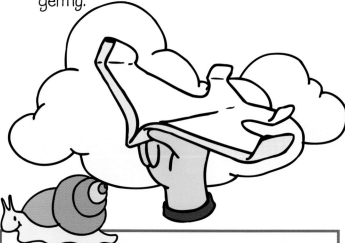

The largest paper airplane ever built was made in 1994 by a group of engineers from BP Chemicals, Ltd. Its wingspan was 40 feet, 6 inches. It flew indoors in Filton, England, for a distance of 77 feet, 4 inches.

Whiny Flyer

*If you listen carefully, you will hear a slight whine
when this toy is flying.*

You'll need:

8 1/2-inch by 11-inch piece of paper
scissors
transparent tape
3 paper clips

1. Fold the paper in half down the middle. In the center of the fold, make a 1/2-inch cut.

2. Keep the paper folded, start at the long side without the cut and roll the paper to make a narrow tube.

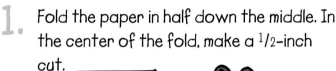

3. Hold one end of the tube so it does not move. Use your fingers to open the other end of the tube a little. Now the tube will look like a cone. The larger end of the cone should be one-inch across.

4. Place a piece of tape near the small end of the cone. Put another piece about 1/4 inch from the cut in the center as shown.

5. Fold up the loose edge of paper from the cut to the wider end of the cone as shown.

6. Slip three paper clips onto the small end of the cone.

7. To launch the whiny flyer, hold it between your pointer finger and thumb. The pointer finger should be on the tail. Quickly move your wrist back and then forward as you let go of the flyer.

Take your kite to an open field on the next warm, windy day.

You'll need:

2 sheets of newspaper
tape
string
large piece of paper
pencil
crayons and markers
glue
colored paper
scissors
kite string
fabric scraps

1. Fold one sheet of newspaper in half. Roll it up tightly to make a pole. Tape it at both ends and in the middle. Do the same with the other piece of newspaper.

2. With the string, tie the two poles together in the middle as shown.

3. Beginning at one end of one of the poles, wrap and tape string to each end to form a kite shape.

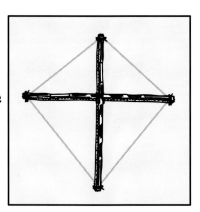

4. Lay the kite frame on top of the large piece of paper. Use a pencil to trace the kite shape, making your tracing larger than the kite frame.

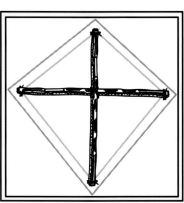

5. **STOP** Cut out the kite shape. Cut off the four corners of the paper as shown.

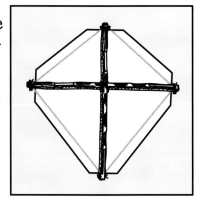

6. Use the crayons, markers, colored paper, and glue to decorate your kite.

7. Lay the kite frame on the back of the kite cutout. Fold the paper over the string on one side of the kite. Tape it down. Do this with the other three sides also.

8. Add a kite string and a tail made out of the fabric scraps.

9. To fly the kite, ask a grown-up to help. Let the grown-up hold the kite. Let out some of the line. While holding the line, stand about 100 feet away from your helper. Your back should be against the wind. When your helper lets go of the kite, reel in the line a little. As the kite rises, slowly let out some more of the line.

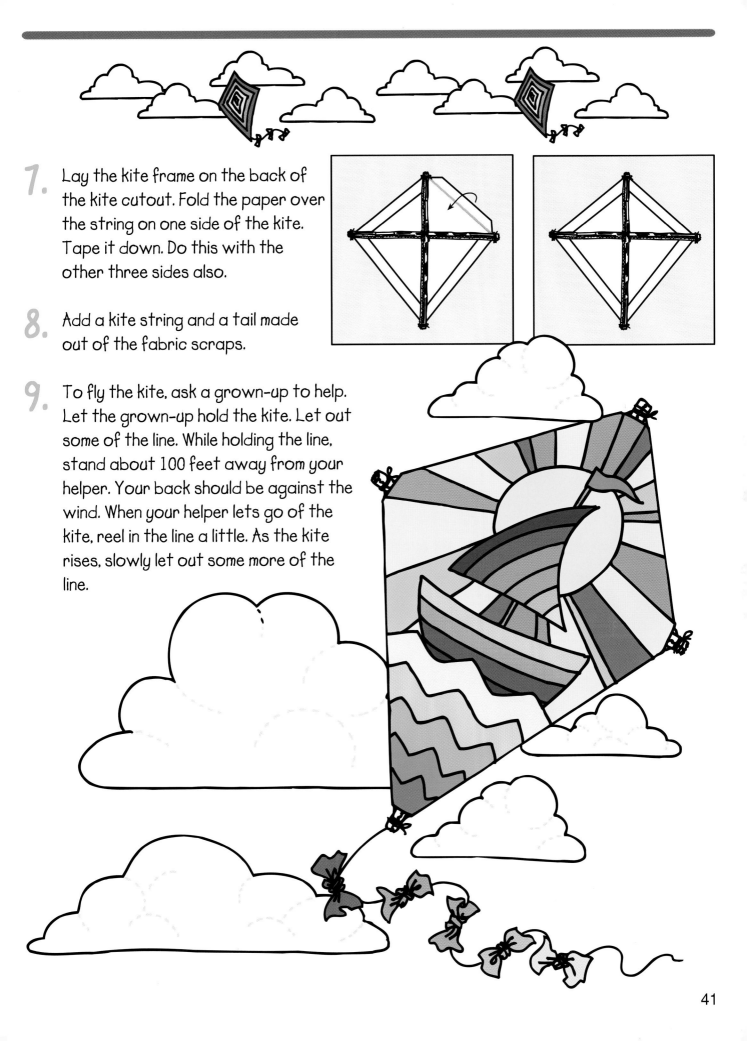

Nature Notes: Clouds

Cloud watching is a relaxing way to spend a lazy afternoon. Lie down in the grass and look up at the sky. What do you see up there? Are the clouds moving? Are they making different shapes? Do you see a cloud that looks like your dog or a car or a house?

Clouds are made of water. As the water at the top of lakes and ponds and oceans evaporates, it becomes part of the air. When water evaporates, it is called water vapor.

Every day when the sun shines down, it warms the ground below it. The air that is near the ground becomes warmer, too. Warmer air weighs less than cooler air. That means the warm air near the ground begins to float up above the cooler air. The water vapor that is in the warm air floats upward with it.

As the air and water vapor move upward, the air begins to cool. The water vapor becomes water droplets again. The water droplets join together, forming clouds.

Clouds change shape a lot. Wind and air can cause this. Sometimes part of a cloud evaporates when it gets mixed with air that has less water in it. Watching clouds move across the sky and change shape can be interesting and fun.

Clouds bring us rain or snow. The water droplets in the clouds turn into ice crystals. When they get big enough, they fall out of the cloud. If the air they fall through is cold all the way down, the droplets stay frozen and we see a snowfall. If they hit warmer air on the way down, the frozen drops become water droplets again and we have rain.

There are different types of clouds. *Stratus* clouds look like sheets. *Cumulus* clouds are piles of fluffy clouds. *Cirrus* clouds are curly or wispy white clouds. Scientists look at the kinds of clouds in the sky, and how high or low a cloud is, to help them forecast the weather.

Try this:
- Keep track of the kinds of clouds you see in the sky every day for a week. Also keep track of the weather every day. Can you tell what kind of weather each type of cloud brings?

Bing Bang Boomerang

With a little practice, your flying boomerang will always come back to you.

You'll need:
empty cereal box
scissors
pencil
tracing paper
gluue
couple of heavy books

1. 🛑 Cut down one side of the cereal box. Open it up so it lies flat.

2. With a pencil, trace the pattern on the next page onto tracing paper. 🛑 Cut out the design from the tracing paper. Trace around the cutout design on one of the large sides of the cereal box. Trace it three more times, so there are four boomerang outlines on the box. Cut out the boomerang shapes.

3. Glue all four cardboard boomerang shapes together. While your boomerang is drying, lay a couple of heavy books on top.

4. Hold your boomerang between your thumb and pointer finger as shown. To throw the boomerang, pull your arm to the back and side quickly. As you bring your arm up toward your head, let the boomerang go into the wind. Throw the boomerang high in the air. If it doesn't come back at first, keep trying. You'll know when you get the throw right!

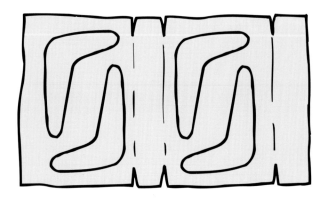

How long do you think your boomerang will stay in the air? The world record is held by Dennis Joyce of the United States. In 1987 he threw a boomerang that stayed in the air for 2 minutes, 59.94 seconds.

Boomerang Pattern

How Does Your Garden Grow?

When you first plant flower seeds, all you see is a big plot of soil. Then one day, you see little shoots of green sticking up out of the ground. Day by day, these shoots get taller and taller. Later they grow buds. One day, those buds become beautiful flowers. It can be very exciting to watch this happen over time.

When you plant your own garden, you get to play in the dirt. You get to squirt the hose. You get to pick the vegetables. So throw on your overalls and get out your rake—it's time to be a gardener!

Basic Gardening Tips

In this chapter there are lots of activities for planting flowers and vegetables. Even when the seeds are different, you have to do many of the same things to the soil and plants. Follow these tips for all the gardening activities in this chapter, unless there are special directions.

1. Before you plant anything outside, be sure it is warm enough. It's best to wait until after the last frost.

2. Wear old clothes and hard-soled shoes to protect your feet.

3. When looking for a spot for your garden, look for a place where the soil has little sand or clay and gets lots of sun. Plants need rich soil for nutrients and sun to help them make their own food.

4. Prepare the soil before you plant. First the soil must be turned with a shovel. Then use a rake. Run it over and over the soil. You want to loosen up the ground and get rid of any hard clumps. Also pull up any weeds that are growing (be sure to get the roots) and take out any rocks. This is the time to add fertilizer if you want. Ask a grown-up to help you with this step. Some fertilizers can be poisonous.

5. Tools you will need: a rake or shovel to turn the soil; a shovel or spade to dig holes for the seeds or seedlings; gloves to protect your hands. You should also wear sunscreen while working in the garden.

6. If you decide to put a plant you started inside in your outdoor garden, set the plant outside for a few days before you replant it.

7. Water plants when the soil feels dry. If you water a plant too much, the leaves will turn yellow and drop to the ground.

Plant a Seedbed

Sometimes you will need to start growing your plants inside.
If you want to get an early start, try making a seedbed, like this one.

You'll need:

empty milk carton
scissors
saucer
pebbles
potting soil
seeds
plastic wrap

1. Wash out an empty milk carton. (STOP) Ask a grown-up to cut out one side of the carton. In the opposite side, punch some holes.

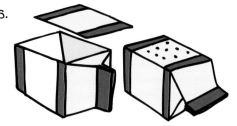

2. Place the milk carton on a saucer, so the side with the holes is facing down. Toss the pebbles into the bottom of the carton. Fill with potting soil until it is 1/4 inch from the top.

3. Plant the seeds. (Read the seed packet to see how deep to plant the seeds.)

4. Spray the soil with water. Cover the carton with plastic wrap.

5. Place the carton in a dimly lit area.

6. When the seeds sprout, take off the plastic wrap.

7. When you water the sprouts, add just enough water until it trickles out the bottom.

8. Plant your seedlings outside when the last frost has passed.

Don't-Bug-Me Sprays

Sometimes bugs can be very pesky. They may eat parts of your plants. Try one of these sprays to keep them away without hurting them.

Knockout Garlic Spray

Keep away caterpillars and other critters that are eating your plants!

Super Soap Spray

This spray will shoo away aphids, very small insects that suck the juices out of plants.

You'll need:

some cloves of garlic
32 ounces water
large bucket
spray bottle

You'll need:

small, leftover pieces of soap
jar
32 ounces cold water
warm water
tablespoon
spray bottle

1. STOP With help, crush the cloves of garlic.

2. Fill the bucket with the water. Put the crushed garlic in the bucket. Let the garlic soak overnight.

3. The next morning, take the garlic out of the water. Pour the water into your spray bottle.

4. Spray the garlic mixture over the leaves of your plants.

1. Place the soap in the jar. Add enough warm water to just cover the soap. Let the soap sit in the water until it becomes jelly-like.

2. Take a tablespoon of the jellied soap and mix it into the 32 ounces of water. Stir the mixture very well.

3. Pour the soap mixture into the spray bottle. Spray the plants wherever you see aphids are living.

Plant a Vegetable Garden

A vegetable garden can keep you very busy, but it's worth it when you taste the delicious things you've grown.

You'll need:

seeds or seedlings
stakes or sticks
string
small shovel or spade
hoe
garden rake
bucket or hose
gloves

1. Ask a grown-up to show you where to plant your garden. You can grow three different kinds of vegetables in a space that is five feet by six feet.

2. Draw a plan of your vegetable garden. Decide what kinds of seeds will go where.

3. Buy your seeds and seedlings. Read the directions to find out when you need to plant them and how to do it.

4. In early spring, prepare your garden. Make a small fence by sticking stakes around the edge of the garden and running string around it. Pull the weeds from the garden. Turn the soil (see page 47, Step 4). If you find any rocks, take them out of your garden.

5. On the day you are ready to plant, water the soil very well. Follow the directions that came with the seeds and plant them.

Carrots

Cucumbers

Tomatoes

6. Mark each row of plants so *you* remember what they are. You can write the name of the seed on a stake and stick it in the soil at the end of the row. Or attach the seed package to a stake and then stick the stake in the soil at the end of the row.

7. When the plants are very small, water them a lot, probably every day. As they get bigger, keep them watered so the seeds will *germinate* (that means they'll sprout). If you feel the soil and it feels damp, do not water the garden. When *you* do water, water just long enough to make the soil moist. You don't want to make big, muddy puddles in your garden! Also be sure to pull out any weeds that start growing.

9. Pick your veggies when they are ripe, probably in about two or three months.

8. Watch your garden grow. Keep insects and animals away. Pull weeds as they pop up.

Tomatoes

Dayton, Ohio, is home to a HUGE community garden that has 952,476 square feet of plants and flowers! You could fit more than 16 football fields into that garden. How big does your garden measure?

Scrappy Scarecrow

A scarecrow will keep the birds and other animals from eating your plants and flowers.

You'll need:

2 broom handles
string
old clothes
old white towel or pillowcase
newspaper
markers or paints
big bells or wind chimes

1. With help, stand one broom handle in your garden area. Push the handle into the ground so it stands.

2. **STOP** Ask a grown-up to tie the other broom handle to the one that is standing to make a cross.

3. Dress the scarecrow in the clothes. Use an old white towel or pillowcase to make a head: stuff it with newspaper, slip it over the top of the standing broom handle, and tie it closed. Draw or paint a face onto the pillowcase. Be sure the clothes are loose enough to flap in the wind.

4. Tie bells or wind chimes to each arm of the scarecrow. The noise will frighten the birds away.

Scarecrows got their names from what they do—they scare away crows (and other birds) so they won't eat the plants in your garden. The Speers family in Ontario, Canada, built a scarecrow in 1989 that was 103 feet, 6¾ inches tall. They had 15 helpers and named their creation "Stretch II."

Salute to String Beans

Some beans grow on vines that climb and need a lot of room.

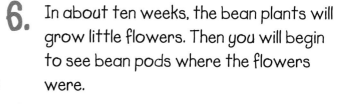

You'll need:
string-bean seeds
string
ruler
tall stakes

1. Find a place to plant your beans.

2. Prepare the soil as directed (see page 47, Step 4).

3. Plant the bean seeds so they are 1/2 inch under the ground and six inches apart. Water regularly.

4. Your seeds will sprout in about two weeks. Thin out your plants by pulling every other sprout out of the ground. You should have 12 inches between plants now.

5. After the seeds sprout, place a couple of tall stakes in the soil around the bean plants. Gently tie several plants to each stake. As they grow, they will lean on the stake.

6. In about ten weeks, the bean plants will grow little flowers. Then you will begin to see bean pods where the flowers were.

7. When the pods grow to three or four inches long, they are ready to be picked.

In 1994 a man in Robersonville, North Carolina, grew a string bean that was 48 inches long! Is this taller than you?

Cream-of-the-Crop Cucumbers

Cucumbers belong to the same family as pumpkins, squash, and melons!

You'll need:

cucumber seeds
ruler

1. Choose a sunny spot to plant your cucumbers. Prepare the soil (see page 47, Step 4).

2. Form little mounds of soil three feet apart. Plant five seeds in each mound. Water regularly.

3. In about ten days, you will see some sprouts. Two weeks after that, thin your seedlings according to the directions on the seed package.

4. Even though you want the soil to be moist, try to keep the leaves dry.

5. When your cucumbers are six to eight inches long (about two months after you thin them), they are ready to be picked.

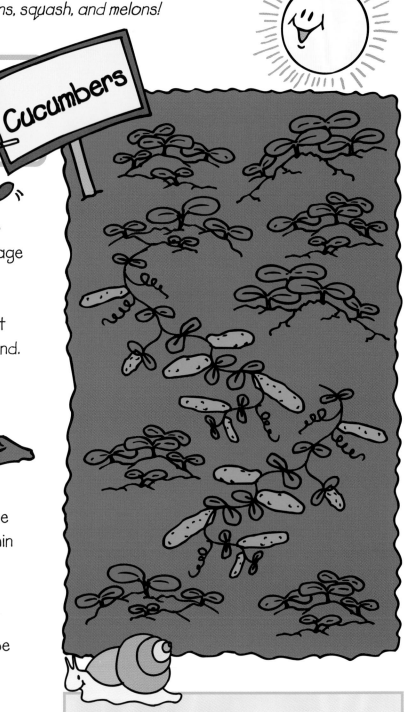

In 1991 a woman in Wales grew a cucumber that weighed over 20 pounds! Wow, what a pickle! Can you name kinds of pickles you can make from cucumbers?

Top Tomatoes

Homegrown tomatoes are much more delicious than the ones you buy in the store.

You'll need:

tomato seeds
ruler
stakes
string

1. Begin a seedbed for your tomatoes about a month before the last frost.

2. Choose a place to plant your tomatoes outside. Prepare the soil (see page 47, Step 4).

3. When the seedlings are about six inches tall, they are ready to be planted outdoors (see page 47, Step 6).

4. Plant the seedlings about two feet apart. When they are 12 inches tall, push a stake into the soil next to each plant. Loosely tie each plant to the stake.

5. Water the plants regularly. The tomatoes should be ready in about eight to ten weeks.

Do you enjoy eating tomatoes? A long time ago they were not a very popular food.

Tomatoes were probably first grown in Peru. The Spanish probably brought the tomato plant to Europe from Mexico. But the Europeans only liked to look at the pretty vine and flowers. They thought tomatoes were poisonous!

Many people thought tomatoes were shaped like a human heart. Eventually the French gave the tomato the name *pomme d'amour*, which means "love apple." One day the French got brave and began using tomatoes in their meals. When the French army was in New Orleans, they ate tomatoes every day. Very slowly, other people began to eat tomatoes, too. The fruit became so popular, people even began to believe that it cured stomach sicknesses. What kinds of foods are made with tomatoes?

55

Nature Notes: Living on a Farm

Farming is a very important job. Most of the food you eat every day comes from farms.

When you think of a farm, you think of people getting up early and milking the cows. You picture farmworkers feeding the chickens by throwing feed into the chicken coop. You guess they tend the fields by guiding their horses along with plows. But very few farms run like that these days.

Today most farms do all that kind of stuff with machines. It is much faster. It also lets farmers grow many more crops than when they did it all by hand. Farmers till, plow, plant, and harvest using machines. Farmers even feed chickens and milk cows without using their own hands!

Farmers must do four main jobs if they want their crops to grow. They are the same things you must do to get your vegetables to grow in the garden. First they prepare the soil by *tillage*, which is the same thing as turning the soil. Then they plant the seeds in the ground. Next they make sure their fields are free of weeds. And when the crops are ready for harvest, they pick them and store them.

In the 1700s and 1800s, most people were farmers. They ate the crops they grew. They worked long, hard hours, doing everything without machines. Sometimes, because of bad weather, they would barely grow enough food to live on.

Today a very small number of people in America work as farmers. But because machines help them grow more food, they can feed everyone with the crops they grow.

There are different kinds of farms. Some farms grow a little bit of everything. Some are dairy farms, where cows give milk for cheese and ice cream. Some are livestock farms where animals like cows, sheep, and pigs are raised. There are fruit farms like the apple farms in New York and the orange groves in Florida. Many farms in the Midwest specialize in growing corn, wheat, and other grains. There are potato farms in Idaho and Maine. And some farms in Florida, Hawaii, and Louisiana grow sugarcane.

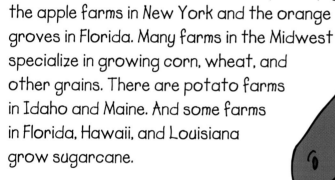

Try this:
- Read a book about farming.
- Visit a farm to see how the crops and livestock are cared for.
- In the early 1900s, a farmer worked about 270 hours to produce 200 bushels of corn. Today a farmer using machines can grow that much with only 12 hours of work. Keep track of how much time you spend working on your garden. See how many vegetables you can grow.

Crazy About Carrots

*You won't see these veggies while they grow,
but you'll have bunches of fun picking them!*

You'll need:
carrot seeds
glass
ruler

1. Pick a spot to plant your carrots. Prepare the soil (see page 47, Step 4).

2. Fill a drinking glass with water. Place the carrot seeds in the glass. Soak the seeds overnight.

3. Plant the seeds $1/2$ inch into the ground. The seeds should be about two inches apart.

4. Water the seeds every day. In 14 to 21 days, the seeds will sprout. Continue watering the plants when the soil is dry.

5. After a month, you need to thin the plants. Pull out the carrot plants so there are four inches between the plants. (You can eat the tiny carrots you pull up.)

6. Ten to 12 weeks later, when you see the carrot tops poking out of the soil, your carrots are ready to be picked.

Carrots originally came from Afghanistan. They were purple and skinny. In the 1700s, Dutch scientists experimented until they grew carrots that were bright orange. Most Americans today eat orange carrots, but in Europe, they still grow yellow, red, white, and purple carrots.

Good Gosh, Great Gourds!

Grow gourds this summer to use as Halloween and Thanksgiving decorations.

You'll need:
gourd seeds
ruler
stakes

1. Wait until the last frost has passed.

2. Pick an area to plant your gourds. Be sure it is a sunny spot. Prepare it by turning the soil (see page 47, Step 4) and getting rid of any rocks.

3. Push the seeds about $1/2$ inch into the soil. Water regularly. Wait until they sprout.

4. When the gourds sprout, they need to be thinned. Follow the directions on the seed package. You should leave 10 to 12 inches between the plants.

5. Next to each gourd plant, push a tall stake into the ground. Gourds grow on vines that like to climb upward.

6. The gourds can be picked in about 10 to 12 weeks. Store them in a cool, dry place. *Gourds are not meant to be eaten.* You can use them to make centerpieces. Or try decorating them like you would a pumpkin.

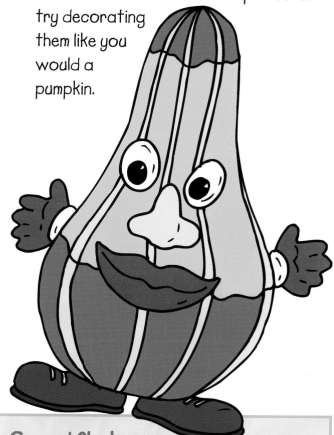

Gourd Shaker
Make a fun musical instrument from a gourd. Ask a grown-up to poke a nail hole into each end of a gourd. Let the gourd dry completely. When it has dried, you can shake around the dried seeds inside to make a noise. Paint your gourd any way you want. Gourds don't last forever, though, so if the shaker starts to smell a little funny, you might want to throw it out!

Pleasing Pumpkin Patch

You can enjoy your pumpkin harvest this autumn!
Make jack-o'-lanterns for Halloween and
pumpkin pies for Thanksgiving.

You'll need:
pumpkin seeds
ruler

1. Prepare the soil
   (see page 47, Step 4).

2. Plant the seeds 1 1/2 inches into
   the ground. Leave three feet
   between the seeds.

3. Water and weed the seeds
   regularly.

4. In 12 to 16 weeks, your pumpkins
   will be orange. When the vines
   begin to die, pick the pumpkins.

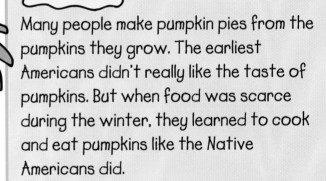

Many people make pumpkin pies from the pumpkins they grow. The earliest Americans didn't really like the taste of pumpkins. But when food was scarce during the winter, they learned to cook and eat pumpkins like the Native Americans did.

The Pilgrims made pumpkin pies, too, but they weren't like the pies you make in your kitchen. The Pilgrims would clean out the inside of the pumpkin. They would drop apples, sugar, spices, and milk inside and put the top back on. Then they would set the pumpkin on the fire ashes and let it bake.

Simply Super Strawberry Barrel

Grow your own delicious strawberries all summer long.

You'll need:

"Everbearing" strawberry plants
old open barrel or wooden box
gravel
mailing tube (with both ends open)
soil
water
ruler

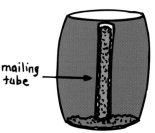

1. 🛑 Ask a grown-up to drill some holes into the barrel. The one-inch holes should be about eight inches apart and scattered around the barrel as shown.

2. Plan to plant your strawberries in the early spring. Place the barrel where you want your strawberries to grow. Once it is filled with soil, you won't be able to move it! Remember, strawberries like lots of sun.

3. Pour the gravel into the barrel until it is two inches deep.

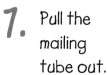
mailing tube

4. Stand the mailing tube inside the barrel. Fill it with gravel.

5. Start filling the barrel with soil. Be sure the mailing tube remains standing in the middle.

6. When the soil reaches the first set of holes, place the roots of a single plant into each hole. Continue filling with soil until you reach the next set of holes and do the same. Water the soil each time you reach a new set of holes. Keep planting, adding soil, and watering until the barrel is full. Plant a few plants on top.

7. Pull the mailing tube out.

Strawberry tips:

- Your berries are ready to pick when they are completely red.
- Your berries will be small the first year.
- During the winter, keep your barrel covered with a heavy piece of plastic.

Mad About Marigolds

Marigolds are pretty orange, red orange, or yellow flowers.

You'll need:

marigold seeds
shovel or rake
empty milk carton
saucer
pebbles
scissors
potting soil
plastic wrap
ruler
plastic bag
envelopes

1. Find a place to plant the marigolds. Prepare the garden by turning the soil (see page 47, Step 4) and taking out any rocks.

2. Start the seeds in an inside seedbed in mid-April (see page 48).

3. After the last frost, plant your seedlings outside (see page 47, Step 6). Leave at least a foot of space between the seedlings. Until the flowers bloom, water the garden regularly—about once a day. Once you see blooms, water the flowers whenever the soil feels dry.

4. At the end of the season, collect seeds from the flowers to plant the following year. To do this, put a plastic bag over a dried flower. Tie it at the bottom. Cut the stem of that flower from the plant. Shake the bag so the seeds fall into the bag. Pour the seeds into an envelope. Write the name of the flower (marigold) on the envelope. Put it in a dry place that's not too hot. Next year, you won't have to buy any seeds.

About marigolds:

There are different kinds of marigolds. Some are small. They grow to be six or seven inches high. They are called *dwarfs*. Other marigolds can grow to be a couple of feet high.

Marigolds are annual flowers. That means that once they die, they don't come back the next season. You will have to plant more marigold seeds the next year.

The best thing about marigolds—besides their beautiful colors—is that they keep bugs away from your garden. Marigolds have a peppery odor that bugs don't like. When bugs smell it, they go away.

Magnificent Zinnias

Colorful zinnias are a snap to grow!

You'll need:

zinnia seeds
rake

1. Be sure the last frost has passed. Prepare the soil as directed (see page 47, Step 4).

2. Throw handfuls of the seeds onto the soil where you want your zinnias to grow. Be sure you choose a place with lots of sunshine. Zinnias like to be warm and sunny.

3. Rake over the zinnia seeds. Be sure to water them regularly.

4. In six weeks, your zinnia seeds will be beautiful flowers!

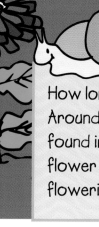

How long have flowers been on Earth? Around 1989, a fossil of a flower was found in Australia. Scientists think the flower grew 120 million years ago! The flowering plant is called a *Koonwarra*.

Sensational Sunflowers

These big, bright flowers can grow taller than you!
They will add a splash of sunny color to your garden.

You'll need:
sunflower seeds

1. Decide where you want to plant your sunflowers. Be sure it is a space that gets lots of sun.

2. Prepare that area by turning the soil (see page 47, Step 4). Get rid of any rocks.

3. In early May, plant the seeds so they are $1/2$ inch down into the ground. The seeds should be about two to three feet apart.

4. Water the seeds every day. When they begin to sprout (in about two weeks), water them whenever the soil feels dry.

In 1986 a woman in the Netherlands grew a sunflower that was 25 feet, $5^1/2$ inches high!

A Peach of a Tree

If you live in a warm area, try growing a pretty peach tree in your backyard.

You'll need:

peach pit
small pot
potting soil
water

1. 🛑 Ask a grown-up to break open the peach pit (actually called a stone). Take the seed out of the center of the pit.

2. Fill the pot with potting soil until it is 3/4 inch from the top. Pat down the soil. Water it.

3. Place the seed on top of the soil in the center of the pot. Pour more soil on top until the soil is 1/4 inch from the rim of the pot. Pat down the soil. Water it.

4. Place the pot in a sunny spot. Keep the soil moist until the seed sprouts. In the spring, after the last frost, transplant your tree into your yard (see page 47, Step 6).

Peaches may have been first grown in China more than 4,000 years ago. The first peach orchards in the United States were planted in 1565 by Spanish explorers in St. Augustine, Florida. Today there are over 30 million peach trees in the United States. Most of the nation's peaches are grown in California.

Nature Notes: How a Greenhouse Works

Some plants have a hard time growing outside. It may not be warm enough. The climate may be too dry. But you can grow all kinds of plants in a greenhouse.

A *greenhouse* is a building made of clear glass or plastic. It has a slanted roof. Greenhouses are also called *hothouses* or *glasshouses*.

People growing plants in a greenhouse can control the temperature, light, moisture, and soil that the plants need. The slanted roof of a greenhouse lets in a lot of sunlight. The greenhouse traps the heat that is produced by the sun. This keeps the greenhouse warm. Sometimes, if it is really cold outside, a greenhouse will use a furnace and pipes to pump hot air into the building.

Greenhouses can be used to start seeds. You may want to get a head start before planting season rolls around. But maybe it is not warm enough outside for seeds to sprout. If you put them in a greenhouse, it will feel like spring and summer to the seeds. They will sprout just as if the weather were warm outside. After the last frost, you can take your seedlings from the greenhouse and plant them outside.

HOLIDAY POINSETTIAS

Greenhouses are also used to grow vegetables out of season. You probably eat tomatoes, lettuce, and cucumbers all year long. But they grow outside only during the regular season. For you to eat a salad in December or January, these vegetables must be grown all year long in greenhouses.

People use greenhouses to grow plants that grow only in certain areas. For example, poinsettias, those pretty plants you see at Christmastime, need to be grown in hot, tropical places. In order for them to be grown in the United States, they need to be kept in greenhouses.

Sometimes, planters will build greenhouses over the plants that are already in the ground. They will use either *cold frames* or *hotbeds*. Cold frames are just plastic or glass and wood boxes that are placed on top of the plants in the ground. They work the same way as greenhouses, keeping the heat inside the box. Hotbeds look like cold frames, but besides the box on top, farmers run electric heating cables under the soil to produce heat inside the box. Once the weather turns warm, farmers remove the cold frames and hotbeds.

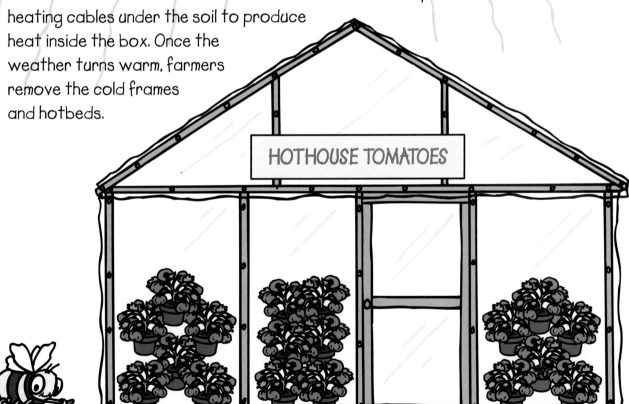

HOTHOUSE TOMATOES

Try this:
- Before the last frost, start some seeds. Plant some in the ground. Plant others in a greenhouse like the one on page 68. Plant a third set in a seedbed like the one on page 48. Which seeds grow the best?

Greenhouse in a Snap

A greenhouse uses the heat of the sun to keep plants warm on cold nights!

You'll need:

wooden planks (two or three inches wide)
hammer
nails
heavy, see-through plastic covering
some large cans with tops
black paint
paintbrush
some bricks
water
seeds or seedlings

1. Find a spot right next to the side of your house or garage. Prepare that spot for planting: turn the soil, pick any weeds, and take out any rocks.

2. Lean the wooden planks up against the house as shown. Leave room between the planks for the plants to grow.

3. Cover the wooden planks with the plastic. It should cover all the planks as well as the sides and should reach from the top to the bottom. STOP Ask a grown-up to nail the plastic to the tops of the planks. The plastic needs to fit snugly enough so that no air can get in.

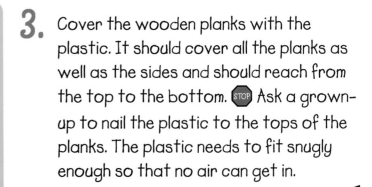

4. Paint the cans on the tops and sides with black paint. Let them dry.

5. Fill the cans with water and put the tops back on. Line them up against the house. The color black attracts sunlight. The sunlight will warm the water in the cans. The warm water will keep the plants warm at night.

6. Plant your seeds or seedlings according to the directions, or follow the steps on page 47.

7. When the day is warm and sunny, keep the plastic pulled up to the top of the planks so the plants will get some direct sun. Each night or when it is cold, pull the plastic over the planks. Pull it tight and place bricks on the bottom to keep it in place.

8. Use your greenhouse to sprout seedlings or grow vegetables all year long.

Planting Bulbs—A Bright Idea!

Some very beautiful flowers grow from bulbs. Each bulb is short stem base with plant buds inside. Tulips, iris, daffodils, lilies, and gladioli grow this way. You need to plant your bulbs in the fall to have beautiful flowers in the spring.

You'll need:

bulbs
shovel
ruler

5. You will see your flowers bloom in the spring.

1. In early fall, take a grown-up to a garden store and buy some bulbs. Decide where you want to plant them. If the bulbs come with any directions, read them.

2. Using a shovel, turn the ground six inches deep. This makes the soil loose.

3. Dig a five-inch hole for each bulb. The holes should be six to eight inches apart. Place one bulb in each hole. If you want, try to make designs with your flowers by planting different kinds of bulbs in a certain pattern. Cover each bulb with soil.

4. Immediately water the ground well. If there is not a lot of rain in the fall, be sure to keep the bulb garden watered.

Birds & Bees & Nests in Trees

You can find all kinds of creatures outdoors—creepy, crawly bugs, slithery worms, colorful birds, and fuzzy squirrels. It can be a lot of fun to take some time to watch our animal friends as they work, play, and eat. It's important not to hurt the animals, so try to watch without getting in their way. Build houses for them or leave out food. You will learn about all the creatures around us.

Wiggly Worm Farm

Spy on the underground world when you keep worms as pets.

You'll need:

clear glass or plastic container
black paper
black tape
soil, sand, dead leaves
shovel or spade
hammer
nail

1. Put the soil, dead leaves, and sand in the glass container. Sprinkle water on top of each layer as you put it in the container.

2. Tape the black paper around the container. Earthworms don't like light, so if the paper isn't there, they stay away from the sides of the container. Then you won't be able to see them. Keep the paper on the glass until you want to look at what the worms are doing.

3. Dig up some earthworms in your backyard. Try going out at night, when they are usually closer to the surface.

4. Place the worms in the container. **STOP** Keep the container covered, but ask a grown-up to punch some holes in the top for air.

5. To feed the worms, put little pieces of lettuce, dead leaves, grass, and tiny bits of table food on top of the soil in the container. Sprinkle a little water on the soil every day. Be sure to take out any old food that the worms don't eat.

Here are some things to look for:
- How do worms move?
- Do worms have feet?
- Do worms have eyes or mouths?
- How long is the average worm?
- If you play the radio next to their container, how do the worms act?
- As earthworms move through soil, the soil passes into and out of their bodies. When it passes out of their bodies, it looks like little piles of dirt. These are called castings. Do you see any?

Worm charmers coax earthworms out of the ground by moving objects in the soil that cause vibrations. In 1980 in England, a man charmed 511 worms out of the ground in 30 minutes. How many worms can you charm?

Admire an Ant

Want to watch ants work together in their colonies? Create an ant farm that lets them live indoors without being pests!

You'll need:

soil
large spoon
large jar with lid
small, narrow jar with lid (that fits inside the larger jar)
hammer
nail
black paper
masking tape
small sponge

1. (STOP) Ask a grown-up to poke very small holes in the lid of the large jar. (The holes should be smaller than ants.) Place the small jar, with the lid on, inside the large jar.

2. With the spoon, dig up some ants in the backyard. Be sure one of them is a queen (she is larger than the others). Place the ants and soil into the large jar.

3. Cover the jar with black paper. Leave the paper on until you want to see what your ants are doing. When you are finished watching, put the paper back on the jar. This keeps out the light, so the ants will tunnel close to the edge of the jar where you can see them.

4. Dampen the sponge. Set it on top of the small jar in the ant farm. Be sure it is always moist.

5. Feed the ants by placing tiny crumbs of food and birdseed on the soil in the jar.

Things to look for:
- How do they carry food?
- Do they spend time together?
- Do they ever sleep?
- Do they stay in one part of the jar more than others?
- Does an ant have eyes, a nose, and a mouth?

Nature Notes: Fireflies

If you see a small, flashing light against the summer night sky, you are probably looking at a firefly.

Fireflies, or lightning bugs, are beetles whose bodies light up. When a living thing glows, it is called bioluminescent (bye oh loo mi NES ent).

There are about 1,900 different kinds of fireflies. They can be found all over the world except in Antarctica. Usually, it is the adult firefly that has a light. But some types of fireflies glow only when they are young. Sometimes these young fireflies with lights are called glowworms.

Fireflies are about $1/4$ to $3/4$ of an inch long. Most are brown or black. They have two sets of wings—one set to fly with and one set to cover the flying wings. Some female fireflies do not fly, so they may not have wings.

The light in a firefly is made by organs in the last section of the firefly's body. A chemical reaction there makes the light appear. This light does not make any heat, though.

When fireflies turn their lights on and off, they are looking for a mate (a kind of husband or wife firefly). Each kind of firefly has its own signal. The males fly around flashing their signals. The female fireflies answer them by flashing back.

Fireflies are in the young larvae stage for one or two years. As an adult, a firefly will live for only 5 to 30 days.

Fireflies are not the only living things that give off light. Some bacteria and fungi glow. And many squids and fish produce light.

Try this:
• Try to catch some fireflies in a jar. Look at them in the light to see what their bodies look like. Then watch them in the dark to see them flash their lights. Don't forget to set them free when you are finished!

Catching Webs

You can make a masterpiece from an empty spiderweb.

You'll need:

black enamel spray paint
white paper
old newspapers
scissors
construction paper

1. Find a spiderweb without a spider.

2. Cover the plants, trees, and grass next to and under the web with the newspaper.

3. Stand about three feet from the web. Spray the web with the paint. Then spray it on the other side. Don't spray-paint it too much, or it will begin to droop from the weight.

4. Lay the white paper behind the web, so that the web fits on the paper. Pull the paper toward you so the web breaks away from what it is attached to. You may need to cut it away if it is too strong.

5. Let the web dry thoroughly. Mount it on construction paper to make a cool decoration.

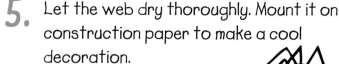

- A spider builds a web quickly and often, so don't worry about destroying its home.

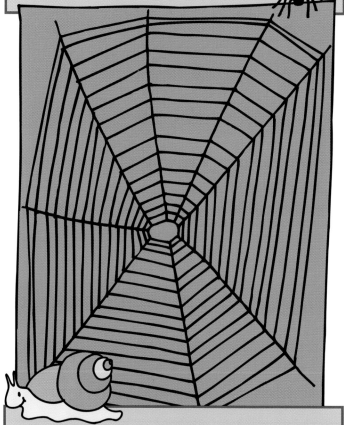

Scientists in England made discoveries in 1990 that helped them decide that animals began living on land about 414 million years ago. Two of the first to crawl around on land were spiders and centipedes!

Building a Better Nest

When birds build nests, they have to fly around looking for twigs and other building materials. Here's a way you can help them out.

You'll need:

pieces of string, fabric, and yarn
wire hanger
string
piece of wide-mesh plastic

1. **STOP** With a grown-up's help, bend the wire hanger into a diamond shape.

2. Tie the mesh to the hanger as shown here.

3. Weave the scraps of yarn and other materials into the mesh.

4. In spring, when the birds are building their nests, hang your creation from a tree, where you can see it. Soon the birds will be flying to your yard for nest materials.

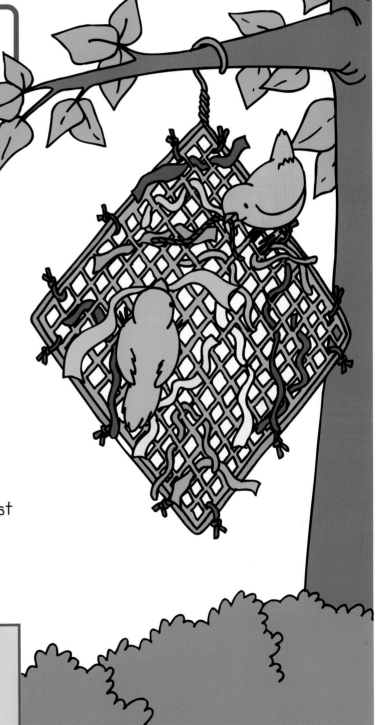

Have you ever found a bird's nest? How big was it? The nest of the mallee fowl in Australia can measure up to 15 feet high and 35 feet across! But nests of hummingbirds can be as small as a thimble!

Nature Notes: Sequoia Trees

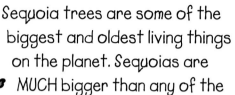

Sequoia trees are some of the biggest and oldest living things on the planet. Sequoias are MUCH bigger than any of the trees that grow in your neighborhood! Millions of years ago, these trees grew all over the earth. Now, they grow only in California.

The first sequoia trees began to grow about 180 million years ago, when dinosaurs lived. It was much warmer on Earth then than it is now. In the last million years, it has grown cooler. This caused many of the sequoia trees to die.

There were once many kinds of sequoias, but now there are two kinds: the redwood and the giant sequoia.

Redwoods grow near the coast of California. The wood from a redwood is pinkish red in color. Redwoods can grow over 300 feet high, which is as tall as a building that has 30 floors in it! You can't even touch their branches, because they are usually about 150 feet from the ground! And the trunk of a redwood can be more than 10 feet around! Have you ever picked a piece of bark off a tree near your house? Well, you couldn't do that with a redwood! A redwood's bark can be 6 to 12 inches deep!

Giant sequoias are sometimes called big trees or Sierra redwoods. They grow on the slopes of the Sierra Nevada mountains in California. They do not grow as tall as redwoods. But their trunks can get very big. Some of them are more than 100 feet around at the very bottoms of their trunks. The largest tree in the world is a giant sequoia named General Sherman. It is 275 feet high and the bottom of the trunk is 103 feet around! You can see it in Sequoia National Park.

Because sequoia trees are so tall, they need thousands of gallons of water every day to stay alive. Even though the sequoias are very big, parts of them are very small. A redwood's leaves are only about $1/2$ inch long. And a giant sequoia's seed is only $1/4$ inch long.

By looking at the number of rings inside a tree's trunk, you can see how old it is. The General Sherman Tree is thought to be 2,200 to 2,500 years old. Another tree that was cut down had rings that dated it back to 1305 B.C.

No sequoia trees have died from old age, disease, or insects, as far as anyone knows. They are very strong trees. Even fire is not an enemy to a sequoia tree; its thick bark protects it from the flames.

Try this:

- Measure the distance around a tree trunk near where you live. How does that compare to a sequoia?
- If you find a stump the next time you go hiking, count the rings to find out how old the tree was when it was cut down.
- Go outside. Using a measuring tape, see what 275 feet (the height of the General Sherman Tree) looks like.

Bleach Bottle Bird Feeder

Here's a simple bird feeder you can make without a hammer and nails.

You'll need:

large, plastic bleach bottle
scissors
glue
aluminum pie pan
heavy string
birdseed

1. **STOP** Ask a grown-up to wash the bleach bottle out completely.

2. **STOP** With help, cut two holes on opposite sides of the bottle as shown.

3. Glue the pie pan to the bottom of the bleach bottle.

4. Tie one end of the string to the bottle handle.

5. Put some birdseed in the bottom of the bottle.

6. **STOP** Ask your helper to hang the bird feeder in the tree using the other end of the string.

Pinecone Bird Treat

Use pinecones to serve up a tasty treat for your feathered friends.

You'll need:

large pinecone
heavy cord
$1/2$ cup salad oil
1 cup peanut butter
2 cups birdseed
paper bag

1. Twist the cord around the pinecone. Tie it tightly. The leftover cord will be used to hang the pinecone.

2. Stir the oil and peanut butter together in a bowl.

3. Spread the peanut butter mixture onto the petals of the pinecone.

4. Pour the birdseed into the paper bag. Place the pinecone in the paper bag. Shake the bag to coat the pinecone with birdseed.

5. With help, tie the cord around a tree branch to hang your pinecone feeder.

Birds come in all shapes and sizes. Some North African ostriches have grown up to nine feet tall and weighed 345 pounds! They could absolutely squash the smallest bird, a bee hummingbird that is about $2 1/4$ inches long (and half of that is the beak and tail!).

Nature Notes: Why Do Birds Fly South?

When the weather turns cooler, you will see many flocks of birds flying together in one direction. You probably know they are flying south for the winter. But why do they go? And how do they get back?

When the birds fly south, they are migrating. Many animals migrate to find better weather and food. It's kind of like taking a vacation—the animals go away for a while, but they always come back home.

When birds fly south, they are looking for more food and warmer temperatures. When it gets cold in the earth's Northern Hemisphere, it is harder for them to live. Many plants die. Other kinds of food may be covered by snow. So they fly to a place where it is still warm. Some birds will fly tens of thousands of miles during their migrations!

Many scientists study how birds and other animals know when it is time to move to a new place. Some think the birds' bodies just know. When birds do migrate, scientists believe they follow the Sun, Moon, and stars to find their way. They also may follow landmarks like rivers or mountains.

There are many kinds of migration. Frogs and toads migrate a few miles from their homes each year to lay their eggs. Some ocean animals migrate every day by moving closer to the water's surface at night and swimming back down deep into the ocean during the day. Some animals that live in the mountains move higher up the mountain during the summer months.

Try this:
- Watch the birds in your neighborhood. When do they fly south? When do they come back? Do they fly alone or in groups? Do they fly at night or during the day?

Track Castings

Make copies of the animal tracks you find on a trail.

You'll need:

16-inch by 2$\frac{1}{2}$-inch cardboard strip
2 paper clips
plastic bowl
quart-size bottle
    of water
2 large cups
    plaster of
    paris
stick
tissue paper

1. Take all the materials you need with you on a hike. (*No one said this was going to be easy!*)

2. Watch for tracks in the dirt, mud, or sand while you are walking. When you find a clear one, clean away any leaves or rocks. Be careful not to smudge the tracks!

3. Bend the strip into a circle shape. Fasten the two ends with the paper clips. Lay the circle on the ground so it surrounds one of the tracks.

4. Pour the plaster of paris into the bowl. Add some water to the plaster of paris. Using the stick, mix in enough water to make a thick cream.

5. Pour the plaster of paris into the cardboard strip mold. Let it dry for about 20 minutes.

6. Lift the hardened plaster of paris, with the cardboard strip still attached, from the ground. Wrap it in tissue paper. Carry it home carefully.

7. When you get home, clean off any mud or soil that is still stuck to the bottom of the cast. On the back of the cast, write the date that you found the track. Write down where you found it. Try to find out what kind of track it is. Make a collection of different tracks.

Nature Notes: Animal Tracks

Can you find these animal tracks on your next hike?

fox

dog

cat

otter

weasel

mouse

rat

shrew

duck

crow

squirrel

horse

deer

sheep

heron

The Outdoor Lab

When you learn about the outdoors, you can be a scientist. When you watch things and test things and see how they change, you are using the scientific method. You can do experiments with weather, plants, animals, and the air around you. And experiments in nature can be so much fun! Try collecting objects, building instruments, and exploring your neighborhood to learn more about the world around you.

Sundial Station

You don't need a watch to tell time—just follow the sun!

You'll need:

round patio block or piece
    of wood
clay
long pencil
ruler
marker
watch
compass

1. Draw a dot in the center of the patio block or wood. Use the ruler to draw a straight line through the center. At one end of the line, write a very small *N* for north.

2. Press a little mound of clay in the center of the circle. Push one end of the pencil into the clay, so the pencil is standing up. You have made a sundial.

3. Find a place where the sun will shine on the sundial all day. Wake up one morning at sunrise. Put the sundial outside. Use a compass to find which direction is north. Place the sundial on the ground so that the end of the line marked with the *N* is pointing toward the north.

4. Each time your watch hits an hour, go outside and see where the shadow of the pencil is on your sundial. Make a mark where the shadow is. Then write down the time, as shown below. Do this every hour, all day, until the sun goes down.

5. You can leave your sundial outside all the time. If you bring it inside, be sure to use your compass to find north again the next time you put it out. Once the times are marked, you can use the outdoor sundial to tell what time it is.

A sundial is thought to be the oldest tool used to measure time. It is believed sundials were used as far back as 2000 B.C. in Babylon.

87

Homemade Weather Vane

Weather vanes show you what direction the wind is blowing.

You'll need:

block of wood
plastic drinking straw
wooden spool
aluminum foil
scissors
crayons or markers
glue
masking tape
heavy cardboard
compass
permanent black marker

1. Glue the spool onto the top of the wooden block.

2. On one corner of the block, write *N* for north. On the opposite corner, use the permanent marker to write *S* for south. Place the block so the *S* is pointing toward you. Write *E* for east on the empty right-hand corner. Write *W* for west on the empty left-hand corner.

3. In between *N* and *W*, write *NW* for northwest. In between *N* and *E*, write *NE* for northeast. In between *E* and *S*, write *SE* for southeast. In between *S* and *W*, write *SW* for southwest.

4. Sketch an animal design on the cardboard. Many weather vanes are shaped like roosters or horse-drawn carriages, but you can draw or trace any animal you like. (STOP) Ask a grown-up to cut out the design. Cover the design with aluminum foil, as shown.

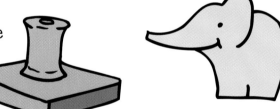

5. Draw an arrow on another piece of cardboard. (STOP) Ask a grown-up to cut out the arrow. Cover the arrow with foil.

6. Tape the animal to the top of the straw. Tape the arrow to the straw underneath the animal. Push the straw into the hole in the spool.

7. Go outside with the weather vane. Use the compass to figure out which way is north or ask an adult to show you. Set the weather vane on the ground so that the north corner is pointing in the same direction as the compass.

8. Keep track of which way the wind is blowing each day. To do this, see which way the arrow is pointing. The wind is blowing from the direction that the front of the arrow is pointing toward. The wind is blowing in the direction that the back of the arrow is pointing to. A wind is always named for the direction it is coming from. For example, a southeast wind is blowing from the southeast toward the northwest.

The windiest place in the world is Commonwealth Bay, George V Coast, Antarctica. Winds reach 200 mph there. If you're not sure how strong 200 mph winds are, remember that hurricane winds start around 75 miles per hour!

Nature Notes: Want to Be a Meteorologist?

When *you* study meteorology, you are studying the weather. Some meteorologists collect information about the weather. Some meteorologists predict what the weather will be like. If you watch the weather person on the evening news, you are probably watching a meteorologist.

If you watch for changes in the wind, temperature, precipitation (rain or snowfall), and air pressure, you can often predict what the weather will be like in the days to come.

The tools for meteorology include thermometers, barometers, and hygrometers. *Thermometers* measure the temperature. *Barometers* measure the pressure in the atmosphere. (The *atmosphere* is the air surrounding the earth.) *Hygrometers* measure the humidity. (*Humidity* is the amount of wetness in the air.)

Some scientists use fancy radar equipment to find and track storms that move over land and sea. They may also use weather *satellites*. These satellites in the sky way above the atmosphere take pictures of the earth. The pictures show meteorologists how the clouds are moving.

A long, long time ago, a man named Aristotle wrote a book about the weather. It was called *Meteorologica*. That's where the word *meteorology* comes from. People began watching the weather scientifically around 1593. In that year, a man named Galileo invented a kind of thermometer. By the end of the 1700s, people had invented tools to measure humidity, wind, air pressure, and rainfall.

People have been weather-watching for a long time. They used the weather to decide when to plant or harvest. Changes in the weather also helped them plan trips and moves. Some changes in the weather were warnings about future storms and disasters. When people noticed those changes, they made plans to move to be safe.

Try this:
- Watch the weather report on the evening news every night for a week. What do you learn about the weather in the future? What is the forecast for next week?
- Track the weather in your neighborhood for a week or two. Find or build tools that let you measure the temperature, rainfall, and air pressure. Record your measurements. Watch for patterns in these measurements and the weather that results.
- Borrow a book from the library about Galileo. What other instruments did he use?

It's a Pond-full!

Build a little pond in your backyard to examine the wildlife inside.

You'll need:

small plastic pool
small fish, frogs, and tadpoles
  you've caught or from the pet store
plants
pond water, if you can get
  it (or use regular
  water)
sand

1. Pour some mounds of sand into the pool to make mini islands.

2. Pour the water into the pool.

3. Place some plants in the pond or plant them in the sand.

4. Place the frogs, tadpoles, and fish in the pond.

5. Watch your pond for a couple of days. What happens? Do the animals change? Do other animals appear in the pond? When you are finished observing, return the animals to their natural homes. Or ask at the local pet store what kind of food and equipment you need to keep them in your house.

Pollution Tester

How clean is the air in your neighborhood?

You'll need:

clear glass dish
petroleum jelly
magnifying glass
tweezers

3. Use the magnifying glass and tweezers to examine the particles that you have collected. What is flying around in the air? Record your answers.

4. Try this experiment at different times of the year and see if you catch different kinds of particles.

1. Spread a layer of petroleum jelly all over the inside bottom of the dish.

2. Place the dish outside on a window ledge. Leave it there for a few days, but do not let it get rained on.

Fancy Fossils

When we study fossils, we can tell a lot about life on Earth thousands of years ago. Try making your own "fossils."

You'll need:

a leaf
heavy, corrugated cardboard
scissors
masking tape
petroleum jelly
plaster of paris
newspapers

1. Cover the table with newspapers.
   (STOP) Ask a grown-up to help you cut out two oval shapes from the cardboard. Draw a smaller oval inside one of the cut-out ovals. Cut out the inner oval to make a frame.

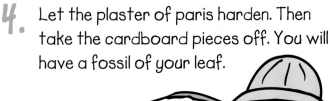

2. Cover both sides of the leaf with petroleum jelly. Place it on the cardboard oval. Place the oval frame on top. Tape the two ovals together.

3. Pour the plaster of paris over the oval so the whole area inside the oval frame is covered.

4. Let the plaster of paris harden. Then take the cardboard pieces off. You will have a fossil of your leaf.

Fossils were made when animals and other living things were covered with volcanic ash. As the ash hardened around the animal, the ash became rock. It made an impression of that animal in the rock. Or ocean animals died and fell to the bottom of the ocean. Their bones or shells formed layers. Layers upon layers were pressed together to form rocks called sandstone or limestone, which are full of fish or shellfish fossils.

Mapmaking

Mapmaking has been around for a long time—since the first explorers. Try making a map of your neighborhood. Just remember, though, things are always changing, so you may have to update your map often.

You'll need:
large piece of paper or brown paper grocery bag
compass
crayons and markers
scrap paper
pencil

1. Decide what you want to make a map of—your street, your school, a park, or another place. Go to that place.

2. Use the pencil and scrap paper to make a sketch of that place. Draw any trees, buildings, special landmarks, playground equipment, paths, and parking lots in your sketch.

3. Notice how big and small things are in relation to each other. Notice how close or far apart they are. Make notes about these things on your sketch. Use the compass to find out the directions. For example, if you are making a map of your street, stand in front of your house with the compass. Which way is north? Put that on your map, as shown above.

4. When you get home, draw your map in pencil on the large piece of paper.

5. Make a legend for your map. A legend is a key for the symbols, as shown at the bottom of the map on this page. For example, you may draw a tree to stand for a park, or a doghouse to show where the dogs in your neighborhood live. You may draw a black line to show roads for cars and a red line to show bike paths. Draw the legend at the bottom of your map.

6. Color in your map. Write the title of your map at the top. Try making a collection of maps for your neighborhood. Put them all together to make a book called an atlas.

The oldest map is a clay tablet that shows the river Euphrates running through northern Mesopotamia (now Iraq). It is believed to date back to around 2250 B.C. The oldest printed map is of western China and dates back to 1115 A.D.

Barometer

Barometers measure air pressure. When the pressure changes, it usually means the weather will change.

You'll need:

plastic container (not more than
8 inches high)
scissors
balloon
rubber band
drinking straw
tape
4-inch by 10-inch piece of poster board
marker
ruler

1. **STOP** Ask a grown-up to cut off a piece of the balloon. Stretch the piece over the top of the plastic container. Wrap a rubber band around the piece of balloon to hold it in place.

2. Lay one end of the straw on the stretched balloon as shown. Tape the straw to the balloon.

3. Fold the poster board in half to make a 2-inch by 10-inch strip. Stand the folded poster board next to the plastic container. Make a mark where the straw crosses in front of the poster board. Write 5 next to that mark. Make five equally spaced marks below the 5 and number them 0, 1, 2, 3, 4. Make five equally spaced marks above the 5 and number them 6, 7, 8, 9, 10.

4. Stand the plastic container and the poster board next to each other. The plastic container is the barometer. The poster board is the scale. You may want to tape the scale to the table or any other surface on which it is standing.

5. Check the barometer at the same time every day. You can check it more than once a day. As the air pressure changes, the straw will move to different marks on the scale.

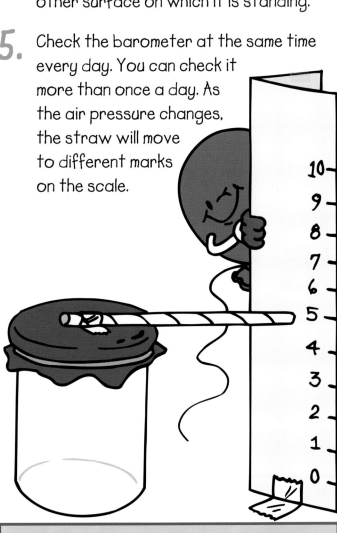

Remember:
In general, lower pressure means the weather is getting cloudier. Higher pressure means the weather is clearing.

Collecting Leaves

Learn about different kinds of trees from the leaves you find.

You'll need:

spiral notebook or photo album
clear tape (if you use a notebook)
guidebook to trees (you can get one in
    the library)
index cards

1. Walk around your neighborhood and look for different kinds of trees. Pick one of the leaves from each tree.

2. Put each leaf on a different page in your book. (Use tape to stick them to the notebook or just slide them into the photo album pages.)

3. Find each leaf in the tree book. On an index card, write down the name of the tree. Write down any other interesting facts about that tree. Attach the index card to that page in your book.

4. Try to find as many different leaves as you can. If your friends collect leaves, see who can find the most. To learn even more about trees, attach seeds and pieces of bark from a tree on the page with its leaf.

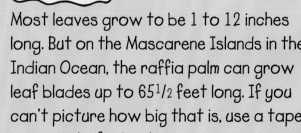

Oak Leaf
This oak leaf turns purplish-red in the fall.

Oak tree seeds are called acorns.
There are many kinds of oak trees.
Some oak trees are over 100 feet tall.

Most leaves grow to be 1 to 12 inches long. But on the Mascarene Islands in the Indian Ocean, the raffia palm can grow leaf blades up to 65½ feet long. If you can't picture how big that is, use a tape measure to find out.

Nature Notes: Why Do Leaves Change Color?

A leaf is a very busy living thing. It works all day long. Leaves must make the food for the rest of a plant.

Leaves contain chlorophyll. That is a pigment that gives the leaf its green color. Chlorophyll is also needed for photosynthesis, the scientific name for the food-making process in plants.

The chlorophyll combines with water, carbon dioxide, and sunlight to make sugar. The sugar is turned into chemical substances, which the plant uses for food. Plants are then used as food for other living things. In fact, all the food that you eat comes from plants or animals that eat plants.

Leaves usually grow to be from 1 to 12 inches long. A plant can have a few leaves or thousands of them. Broad leaves, which most plants have, are wide and flat. Narrow leaves are long and thin. And needle leaves look like needles, like the kinds you see on pine trees.

When leaves first begin to grow, they appear as buds. It can take up to several weeks for a leaf to reach its full size. While it is growing, a leaf changes color. It starts out bright green and then gets duller as it grows. There are other colors inside a leaf, but you don't see them because there is so much chlorophyll, it makes the leaf appear green.

When the summer turns into fall, the days become shorter and cooler. In the cool air, the chlorophyll starts to break down. When it does, the other colors in leaves can show through. The leaves start turning yellow, red, and orange.

When the chlorophyll breaks down, the leaf cannot make food anymore. It dies. The cells that hold the leaf to the plant die. The leaf falls to the ground. Bacteria and fungi on the ground eat the leaf. What is left of the leaf becomes part of the soil. The leaf will become nutrients for new plants.

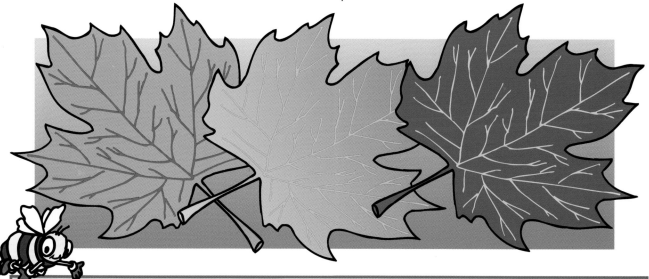

Try this:
- Find a broad leaf, a narrow leaf, and a needle leaf. Compare them.
- Collect a leaf bud, a new leaf, and a dead leaf from a tree over time. Compare the changes in the leaves.
- Examine several dead leaves from the same tree. How many colors come out on every leaf when the chlorophyll breaks down?

Rain, Rain, Gauge Away!

This simple instrument will tell you how much rain falls in your neighborhood.

You'll need:

empty 2-liter plastic bottle
scissors
permanent marker
ruler
wooden stake
large rubber bands
hammer

1. (STOP) Ask a grown-up to cut off the top third of the bottle. Lay the bottle top upside down on top of the open end of the bottle, as shown.

2. Use the ruler to mark off measurements on the bottle. Stand the ruler next to the bottle. Make a mark at the 1/4-inch point. Write 1/4 next to it. Make a mark at the 1/2-inch point. Write 1/2 next to it. Do this for 3/4, 1, 1 1/4, 1 1/2, 1 3/4, and 2.

3. Find a flat, open area outside. (STOP) Ask a grown-up to hammer the stake into the ground. Place the rain gauge next to the stake. Wrap the rubber bands around the stake and rain gauge to keep the rain gauge in place.

4. Check your rain gauge every day. When there is water in it, write down how much. Be sure to dump out any water every day after you check it.

The wettest place in the world is Mawsynram in India. Each year, an average of 467 1/2 inches of rain falls there.

The wettest state in the United States is Louisiana, where an average of 56 inches falls every year.

Hygrometer

A hygrometer is an instrument that measures the amount of humidity, or moisture, in the air. Early American farmers made big hygrometers by hanging broom handles from the roofs of their barns. For this hygrometer you will need a friend with long hair!

You'll need:

clear, widemouthed jar
a single strand of hair a few inches
    longer than the jar
red marker
toothpick
glue
pipe cleaner
black marker

4. When the weather is sunny, notice which way the red end of the toothpick is pointing. Draw a sun with a black marker on that side of the jar. When it is raining, notice which way the red end of the toothpick is pointing. Draw rain clouds on that side of the jar.

1. Color one end of the toothpick red. Wrap one end of the hair around the center of the toothpick. Place a drop of glue on the toothpick to keep the hair in place. Let it dry.

2. Bend the ends of the pipe cleaner so it sits on top of the jar as shown.

3. Place the toothpick in the jar by holding the end of the hair. The tooth-pick should be in the center of the jar, just above but not touching the bottom. Glue the hair to the pipe cleaner to keep it in place.

Starwatch

Once you've found the Moon, start discovering other heavenly bodies.

You'll need:

telescope or binoculars
notebook
pencils
flashlight
book about stars

1. **STOP** Ask a grown-up to take you outside on a clear, dark night. Find a place where it is very dark, where there are no street or house lights.

2. Just look at the stars! You can use your book to help you find specific stars in the sky.

Here are some tips:

- Stars move slowly. They twinkle. If you see a steady light moving fast, it is probably a satellite or plane. Try using your book to find *Sirius*, *Antares*, *Spica*, *Capella*, *Betelgeuse*, and *Altair*.
- *Polaris*, the North Star, is always in the same place. You will find it if you look to the north. It is also the last star in the handle of the Little Dipper.
- Try to spy some planets. Venus is very bright and can often be seen right after the Sun sets. Mars is a reddish light. Jupiter is a white, steady light. Saturn is a yellow light.
- If you see a streak in the sky, you are probably seeing a shooting star, or meteor. These are usually spotted after midnight. Meteor "showers" occur in August.
- Constellations are groups of stars that make shapes in the sky. Some of those constellations are shown on these two pages.
- The largest star is Betelgeuse. Its diameter is 400 million miles, about 500 times bigger than the Sun!

Nature Notes: The Stars

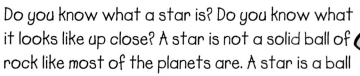

Do you know what a star is? Do you know what it looks like up close? A star is not a solid ball of rock like most of the planets are. A star is a ball of gas. Stars group together in galaxies. The Sun and the Earth belong to a galaxy called the Milky Way.

The Sun is a star. It looks pretty big, doesn't it? It looks much bigger than the stars you see in the sky at night. But the Sun is only a medium-size star. Many stars are much bigger. Even so, the Sun is 109 times bigger around than the Earth!

The Sun looks so much bigger than the stars you see at night because it is closer to the Earth than those other stars. The star closest to the Earth after the Sun is 25 million million miles away. It would take a million years to fly that far in the fastest jet!

Some stars are brighter than others. Some look yellow, blue, red, or white. The color and brightness of a star depends on its size and temperature. When you study stars, the Moon, and the planets, you are studying astronomy.

The stars shine in the sky day and night, but we rarely see them during the day. Sunlight shines so bright during the day that it is hard to see the other stars. When we do see the stars at night, they seem to twinkle on and off. They twinkle because the light they give off has to pass through layers of moving air. That means the light does not pass straight from the star to our eyes. It gets broken up a little, so the star looks like it is twinkling.

Scientists guess that there are 10 billion trillion stars in the universe. Only about 6,000 stars can be seen from the Earth without a telescope. Scientists think that most of the stars we see started shining about 10 billion years ago. But new stars are still being created today.

Before people had watches and calendars, they used the stars to tell time. By watching the Sun, Moon, and stars, people knew when to plant crops and could predict what the weather would be like. People also used stars to tell what direction they were moving while traveling. Some people still believe that by studying the stars, they can predict what is going to happen. This is called astrology.

Try this:
- Study a book on astronomy. Try to find the constellations in the night sky.
- Visit a planetarium to learn more about the stars.
- Look at a star with just your eyes. Now look at the star using a telescope. How much better can you see?

Moonwatching

Follow the Moon for a month to learn about its phases.

You'll need:

calendar for this year that does
   not show the Moon phases
pen or marker

1. Every night for a month, look out the window to see the Moon.

2. Each night, draw a picture of the Moon in the space for that date on the calendar. Draw the Moon exactly as you see it outside. (Some nights may be too cloudy to see the Moon.)

3. After watching the Moon for a month, try to guess what the Moon will look like each night for the next month. Draw your guesses on the calendar. Check during the month to see if you were right.

Try to find the answers to these questions:

Does the Moon ever change color?

How many days is the Moon waxing (getting bigger)?

How many days is the Moon waning (getting smaller)?

How many days does the Moon stay full?

How early in the evening can you see the Moon?

When the Sun is directly over the Moon, the temperature in some areas of the Moon can reach 243°. At sunset, the Moon's temperature dips to 58°. And during the night, it drops as low as -261°!

On-the-Trail Tasties

When you go camping or hiking, it's always a great idea to take along a snack. You may want to pack a delicious treat made from veggies and fruits you've grown in your own garden. Or maybe you want to try cooking a campers' meal. Try some of these recipes the next time you are craving some outdoor munchies.

Hot Cocoa with Whipped Cream and Orange Ice Pops

SUGAR

S'mores

Try these great campfire snacks on your next camping trip.

(STOP) An adult should ALWAYS be around when you are near a campfire.

You'll need:
marshmallows
chocolate bars
graham crackers
long sticks
a campfire

1. Place a piece of chocolate on top of a graham cracker.

2. (STOP) Ask a grown-up to help you toast two marshmallows over the campfire.

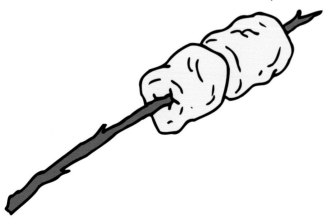

3. Place the two marshmallows on top of the piece of chocolate. Cover the marshmallows with another graham cracker.

4. Gently press down on the s'more to keep it closed. When the chocolate starts to melt, it's ready to eat!

He didn't bring s'mores, but...
In India, Mastrum Bapu camped out by a road in the village of Chitra for 22 years, from 1960 to 1982.

Great Gorp!

*Gorp is a fancy name for trail mix.
It's the perfect snack to take along on a hike.*

You'll need:

nuts
chocolate or carob chips
coconut
shelled sunflower seeds
dried fruit
popcorn
banana chips
cereal
M&Ms®
...or any other kind of munchies
   that tickle your fancy!

1. Mix everything together.

2. Store it in a zippered plastic bag.

How far do you usually hike? Arthur Blessit, from Florida, has walked 30,520 miles since December 25, 1969! He has been to all the continents, carrying a 12-foot cross as he goes.

Groovy Granola

Granola is an easy-to-pack snack you can take on all your outdoor adventures.

You'll need:

3 cups uncooked oatmeal
1 cup nuts
1/2 cup sunflower seeds
1/4 cup sesame seeds
1/2 cup wheat germ
1/2 cup raisins
1/2 cup honey
1/2 cup vegetable oil
2 teaspoons cinnamon

1. Mix together all the ingredients except for the raisins.

2. Spread the mixture on a cookie sheet. **STOP** Ask a grown-up to bake the granola in a 300° oven for 30 minutes. Ask your helper to stir the granola often while it is baking.

3. **STOP** Take the cookie sheet out of the oven. Mix the raisins with the granola. Let the mixture cool completely.

4. If you want to store your granola, put it in a container with a lid that fits tightly.

110

Sunny Fruit Cups

Looking for a natural outdoor dessert?
Try eating grapefruits and oranges warmed by the sun.

You'll need:

2 tablespoons honey
1 grapefruit
1 orange

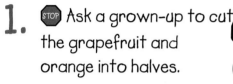

1. STOP Ask a grown-up to cut the grapefruit and orange into halves.

2. Use a spoon to take the fruit sections out of the skin. STOP If you need help, ask a grown-up to use a knife to cut out the sections.

3. STOP Ask your helper to cut out anything that remains inside the fruit skins.

4. Mix the fruit sections in a bowl with 1 tablespoon of honey.

5. Put half the fruit mixture into one grapefruit skin half. Put the rest of the mixture into the other grapefruit skin half. Drizzle a little honey on the top of each grapefruit cup.

6. Cover the grapefruit halves with plastic wrap. Place them on a cookie sheet. Place the cookie sheet out in the sun. Let the fruit cook for a while, until it is as warm as you want it.

Summer Sidewalk Eggs

Is it hot enough to cook eggs on the sidewalk?

You'll need:

margarine
2 eggs
aluminum foil

1. Pull a piece of foil off the roll. You need at least a six-inch-square area for each egg.

2. Rub the *margarine* on the foil so it is well-greased.

3. Find the hottest spot on the sidewalk. Place the foil on that spot.

4. Break the eggs onto the foil. Let them cook. The amount of time they need to cook depends on how hot the sun is. Let them cook until the edges are brown and the yolk is not runny. If you are not sure if they are done, ask a grown-up.

5. Use a spatula to lift the eggs off the foil and onto a plate.

Iced Sun Tea

The sun will help you brew a delicious glass of iced tea.

You'll need:

2 tea bags
quart-size jar
quart of cold water
crushed mint leaves or
    2 cinnamon sticks
lemon
honey

1. Pour the water into the jar. Add the tea bags. Screw the lid on tight.

2. Place the jar outside in a sunny spot. Let it sit for three hours, or until it becomes dark in color.

3. Add the mint leaves or cinnamon sticks.

4. When you serve the tea, pour it into glasses with ice. Add lemon and honey.

Nature Notes: Food

You probably get your food from restaurants and grocery stores. But for thousands and thousands of years, nature and dinner were very closely connected.

If you lived in prehistoric times, you would have searched for your own food. You would have spent most of your day searching for plants, mushrooms, nuts, seeds, roots, and berries to eat. There would be very little time left over for anything else.

The earliest people did not hunt. They did not farm. They did not have fire. So they didn't have lots of different foods to choose from.

When early people learned to make tools, they began to hunt. And eventually they discovered fire. Then they could add small animals and roasted foods to their menu.

Early people could not live in one place all the time. Eventually, they would use up all the food. Or the weather would change, and the food would stop growing where they lived. When this happened, the families would walk and walk and walk until they found a new place with a steady food supply. People who move around looking for food are called nomads.

Very slowly, people started spending more and more time in one place. They learned how to control the food they ate. They realized they could plant the seeds from the plants they ate and grow new plants. They discovered they could capture young wild animals and raise them.

About 9000 B.C., the first farmers began raising some of their own food. They lived in a place called the Fertile Crescent. Today, that area covers Lebanon and parts of Iran, Iraq, Israel, Jordan, Syria, and Turkey. At first, farmers ate the crops they grew along with the food they would hunt for. They grew grains, like barley and wheat, and raised animals like goats, sheep, and cattle.

For a long time, people still spent much of their day growing and finding their own food. Most people in the United States grew their own food through the 1800s. And even today, farming is still the most important job in some countries.

Try this:
- Read a book about prehistoric people.
- Search in your neighborhood for foods you could eat for dinner (but don't pick them and DEFINITELY don't eat them). How much did you find? If you were a nomad, would you be able to stay in your neighborhood?
- Plant a small garden. Keep track of how much time you spend in the garden and how much food you grow. Think about how much bigger your garden would have to be to feed your whole family for the year. How much time would you have to spend working on it every day?

Sidewalk Cinnamon Toast

This takes a while to make, so you may just want to try this when you are spending some time outside.

You'll need:

2 thick slices of bread
margarine
cinnamon-sugar mixture
plastic wrap

1. Spread the margarine onto the bread slices. Sprinkle both sides of each slice with the cinnamon-sugar mixture.

2. Wrap each slice in the plastic wrap. Place the slices on a very hot spot on the sidewalk.

3. After 30 minutes, turn the slices over so the other sides are facing up. Leave the slices in the sun for another 30 minutes. Then enjoy!

Dried Apples

*Mix dried apples with raisins, nuts, and coconut
for a new kind of trail mix.*

You'll need:

apples, peeled and cored*
cheesecloth
old sheet

5. Store the slices in zippered plastic bags.

1. Ask a grown-up to help you slice the apples into rings.

2. Throw the sheet over a picnic table. Be sure the table is sitting in the hot sun.

3. Arrange the apple slices on the sheet. Cover them with the cheesecloth.

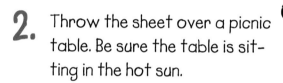
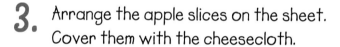

4. When the tops of the apple slices are dry, turn the slices over. When both sides of the apples are dried, they are ready. This will take several days. Be sure to bring the apple slices inside at night so the dew does not make them moist.

* You can also try this with peaches, pears, and apricots.

Some people use dried apples to make apple pie, but the biggest apple pie ever was made with regular apples. In Chelsfield, England, in 1982, a chef baked an apple pie that was 40 feet by 23 feet! It took three days, and contained over 600 bushels of apples. The pie weighed 30,115 pounds!

117

Jammin' Solar Spread

Use the sun to make a delicious batch of strawberry jam.

You'll need:

1 cup sugar
1 tablespoon lemon juice
1 pound strawberries with stems removed
plastic wrap

1. Place the berries in a saucepan. Cover the berries with the sugar. Add the lemon juice. Put a cover on the saucepan. Let the mixture sit for an hour.

2. (STOP) Ask a grown-up to heat the saucepan on a stove until the mixture comes to a boil. Let the mixture boil for about five minutes. Take the berries off the stove and let them sit for another hour.

3. Spoon the mixture into a shallow baking dish. Cover the dish with plastic wrap.

4. Find the sunniest spot outside. Set the pan in that spot. Leave it there all day.

5. Pour the jam into a jelly jar. Store it in the refrigerator.

Campers' Carrot Cake

Make this dessert favorite from the carrots you grow in your garden.

You'll need:

1 1/2 cups grated carrots
1 1/3 cups water
1 1/2 cups brown sugar
1 cup raisins
1 teaspoon cinnamon
2 teaspoons butter
2 teaspoons baking soda
2 cups whole wheat flour
1/2 teaspoon salt
1/4 cup powdered sugar

1. Place the carrots, sugar, raisins, and water in a saucepan. (STOP) Ask a grown-up to bring the water to a boil. Boil the mixture for eight minutes. Remove from the heat.

2. Add the butter and cinnamon to the saucepan. Add the baking soda, flour, and salt. Mix well.

3. Pour the batter into a loaf pan or a 9-inch square pan. (STOP) Ask your helper to bake the cake at 375° for 45 minutes.

4. When the cake is completely cooled, sift the powdered sugar on top.

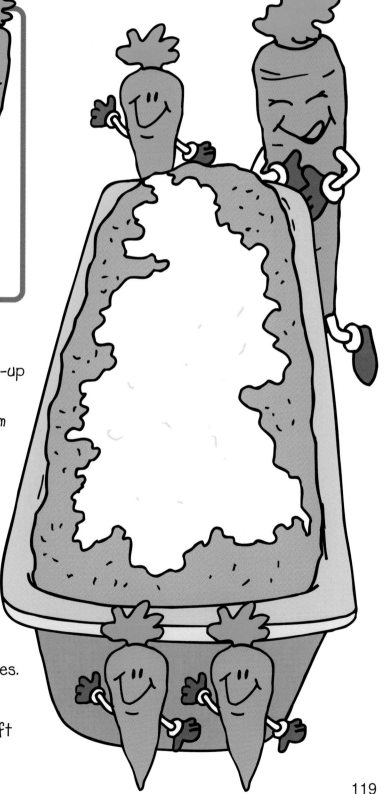

Very Hearty Veggie Soup

Here's a delicious way to carry your vegetables along on a hike.

You'll need:

vegetables from your garden: carrots, potatoes, tomatoes, beans, peas, zucchini, onions, corn, peppers, etc. (Have a grown-up help you wash, peel, and chop them up.)

bouillon cube, dissolved in boiling water

1. Place the vegetables in a casserole dish.

2. Cover the vegetables with the bouillon.

3. Cover with a lid. Place the dish in a microwave oven. Turn the microwave on High for 15 minutes, or until the vegetables are tender.

4. Carry your soup in an insulated jug or Thermos® bottle.

Flower-ful Cake Decorations

Use these sweet flowers to decorate a cake.

You'll need:
rose petals
violet blossoms
egg white
1/2 cup sugar

3. Dip the blossoms in the egg white. Lay them on paper towels.

4. Sprinkle sugar on top of the petals and blossoms. Shake on a lot, so they are covered. Let them dry.

5. Shake the flowers so the extra sugar falls off. Decorate cakes with these pretty flowers.

1. Pick the flowers early in the morning. Gently wash the petals and blossoms. Shake off the extra water. Lay the petals and blossoms on paper towels to dry.

2. 🛑 Ask a grown-up to beat the egg white until it is stiff and frothy.

Fruit Chew

This snack will remind you of Fruit Roll-Ups®. It's a great treat to tuck into your knapsack for a hike.

You'll need:

2 quarts of fresh berries, rinsed

1/4 cup sugar

waxed paper

masking tape

1. Place the berries in a saucepan. Mix in the sugar.

2. (STOP) Ask a grown-up to cook the berries over low heat until they are soft. Then pour off any extra juice.

3. Let the mixture cool until you can handle it.

4. Press the berry mixture through a sieve or colander.

5. Lay a large piece of waxed paper outside on a flat surface. Tape down the edges so it won't blow away.

6. Pour the berry mixture onto the waxed paper. Let it dry for a couple of days. It is ready when it easily peels away from the waxed paper.

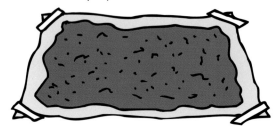

7. (STOP) Ask your helper to cut the fruit chew into strips. Store the strips in a closed container where it is cool.

Winter Cream

Try this cool, special treat after a big snowfall!

You'll need:
bowlful of CLEAN snow
sugar
vanilla extract
milk or cream
hot cocoa mix (optional)

1. Sprinkle some sugar on top of the snow.

2. Add a dash of vanilla.

3. Add a little milk or cream. If you want, sprinkle some hot cocoa mix on top.

4. Stir the mixture together. Eat with a spoon!

SUGAR

Outdoor Café

Share some outdoor treats with your friends and neighbors.

You'll need:

small table or sturdy box
chairs
ice chest with ice
paper or Styrofoam® cups
napkins
poster board
markers
food and drinks to sell

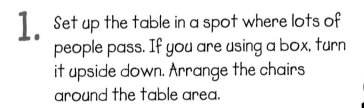

1. Set up the table in a spot where lots of people pass. If you are using a box, turn it upside down. Arrange the chairs around the table area.

2. Decide what you are going to sell. Keep the food and drinks in the ice chest. If you are selling warm drinks or soups, keep them in a Thermos®.

3. On the poster board, make a list of the foods you are selling. Write down the price for each item.

4. Place the sign on the front of the table. Now you're open for business!

Hot Cocoa with Whipped Cream and Orange Ice Pops

Nature Art

Many artists create art that is part of the outdoors. You may see their sculptures in parks. You may admire beautiful buildings that are workplaces, shops, museums, churches, or homes. Some artists show nature in their art. Georgia O'Keeffe painted beautiful flowers. Claude Monet loved to create his paintings while sitting outside. You can use nature to make art, too. You can use flowers, sand, grass, the sun, and many things you find outdoors to make pictures and sculptures.

Sand Sculpture

Instead of store-bought clay, try this mixture for making your own sculptures.

You'll need:
2 cups sand
1 cup water
1 cup cornstarch
food coloring (optional)
stones, sticks, yarn, buttons, and other items to decorate the sculpture

1. Mix all the ingredients together in a saucepan.

2. **STOP** Ask a grown-up to heat the mixture until it gets thick. Stir continuously.

3. Let the mixture cool. Use your hands to shape the mixture into your sculpture. Use the stones, sticks, and other objects to decorate the sculpture.

4. Let it dry completely.

On July 26, 1989, a sand sculpture called "Invitation to Fairyland" was built in Kaseda, Japan. It was 56 feet, 2 inches tall and was built by 2,000 volunteers!

Pinecone Christmas Tree

This tree makes a pretty table centerpiece for Christmas dinner.

You'll need:

lots and lots of small pinecones
cardboard circle
glue
Styrofoam® cone
berries, pine needle clusters, white
    spray paint

5. If you want, spray the white paint in spots to make the tree look like there is snow on it. Be sure to do this outside!

1. Glue the Styrofoam® cone to the cardboard circle.

2. Glue pinecones around the cardboard circle.

3. Starting at the bottom, glue pinecones to the cone until it is covered. Let it dry completely.

4. Glue berries and pine needle clusters to the tree to decorate. Try to slide the pine needles in between pinecones so they look like they are part of the tree.

Nature Notes: The Art of It

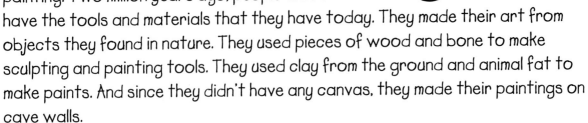

Nature and art have been mixed together ever since people first started drawing and painting. Two million years ago, people did not have the tools and materials that they have today. They made their art from objects they found in nature. They used pieces of wood and bone to make sculpting and painting tools. They used clay from the ground and animal fat to make paints. And since they didn't have any canvas, they made their paintings on cave walls.

Since that time, artists have often used the outdoors for creating and showing their work. Artists have carved images into mountains, like Mount Rushmore in South Dakota and Stone Mountain in Georgia. They created elaborate buildings that were beautiful to look at, like cathedrals and pyramids. They raised giant statues like the Statue of Liberty.

Even though there is a lot of art outside, most art is made and kept inside. For many years, artists worked in studios, painting pictures and sculpting statues that were meant to hang inside houses and churches. Even when their paintings were scenes from the outdoors, they usually created the pictures while they were inside.

Many artists sketched their outdoor scenes while outside. Then they would go inside to paint the pictures in their studios. But the *Impressionists* liked to do their painting in the open air. They liked to use natural light. In fact, Claude Monet, one of the most famous Impressionists, sometimes painted the same scene over and over at different times of the day and year to see how the light changed.

Try this:
- Try to find objects in your backyard that you could use as art tools and materials.
- Try to create a work of art from something in nature, like Mount Rushmore.
- Work like the Impressionists. Paint a picture of the outdoors while you are outside. Try painting the same scene at different times of the day. How does the changing light change your pictures?

Flower Candles

Flowers add a beautiful touch to burning candles.

You'll need:

quart- or half-gallon-size square milk
    carton, rinsed and dried (your candle
    will be as wide as the container is)
cooking oil
paper towel
tuna fish can
paraffin
old candle
flowers
double-stick tape
scissors

1. Press the flowers. See the directions on page 133.

2. (STOP) Ask a grown-up to cut off the top half of the milk carton. Dip a paper towel into the cooking oil. Rub the towel around the inside bottom and sides of the milk carton.

3. Stand the candle in the center of the milk carton bottom. Use the double-stick tape if it won't stand up.

4. Fill the tuna fish can with water. Set the can in a saucepan. Fill the sauce-pan halfway with water. Place a smaller saucepan inside the first, so it sits on top of the tuna can. Place the paraffin inside the smaller saucepan.

paraffin

5. Set the pans on a stove burner. (STOP) Ask a grown-up to melt the paraffin over medium heat.

6. Arrange the dried flowers along the inside of the carton around the old candle. (STOP) Ask your grown-up helper to pour the melted paraffin into the carton while holding the old candle in place. Let the candle harden overnight.

7. Peel away the milk carton to see your candle.

Flower Frame-Ups

Cover your walls with beautiful framed flower designs.

You'll need:

picture frame with glass and
    cardboard backing
solid-color cloth
scissors
tweezers
glue
dried flowers (see the directions on
    page 132)

1. 🛑 Ask a grown-up to help you cut the cloth so it is the same size as the cardboard backing. Glue the cloth to the cardboard. Let it dry.

2. Arrange the flowers on the cloth backing. Use the tweezers to move delicate petals and leaves.

3. Add dots of glue to the back of some of the petals to keep the arrangement in place. Let the glue dry completely.

4. Slip the cardboard into the frame.

Bouquets are bunches of flowers that are used for decorations, especially at weddings. In 1994, a group of people in Victoria, British Columbia, made a bouquet with 10,011 roses. It was 41.9 feet long!

Dried Flower Bouquets

Try these two ways to dry flower bouquets.
These flowers will look beautiful all year long.

Method 1

cornmeal
borax
long, shallow box with top
paintbrush
leaves, flowers, grasses to dry

Method 2

flowers with long stems
string
wire hanger
scissors

1. Mix together equal amounts of cornmeal and borax.

2. Spread the mixture on the bottom of the box, so it is one inch thick.

3. Place the flowers on top of the mixture in a single layer.

4. Sprinkle more of the mixture on top of the flowers.

5. Place the top on the box. Put the box in a dry place. Leave it for about three weeks.

6. Remove the dried flowers from the mixture. Use the brush to dust off the extra mixture from the petals and leaves.

7. Arrange the flowers in vases or baskets to place around your house.

1. Pull all the leaves off the flowers.

2. Tie the flower stems tightly together.

3. Hang the flowers from the hanger, so they are upside down, in a dark, dry place. Leave them for about two weeks.

4. When the flowers are dried, arrange them in a vase. Or tie them with ribbon at the bottom and place them in an empty basket. They also look pretty if you hang them on a wall.

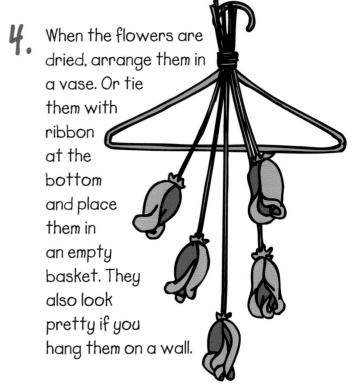

Pressed Flowers

You may want to press your flowers as well as dry them. You can use these flowers to decorate gifts, glue onto notecards, or even decorate birthday cakes.

You'll need:

waxed paper
newspapers
flat boards
bricks
scissors
flowers

1. **STOP** Fold a large piece of waxed paper in the middle.

2. Place the flowers in a single layer on one half of the folded waxed paper. Fold over the other side to cover the flowers.

3. Place the waxed paper on top of some sheets of newspaper. Place some more sheets of newspaper on top of the waxed paper. Place a flat board over the newspaper. Continue layering newspaper, waxed paper, and boards until all your flowers are in the stack. Place the bricks on top.

4. Let the stack sit for three weeks. Carefully remove the waxed paper from the stacks. When you want to use your dried flowers for projects, gently peel away the waxed paper.

133

Nature Notes: Rainbows

Would you like to touch a rainbow or catch a bit of one and put it in your pocket? You probably won't have much luck. Rainbows are not physical objects that you can touch. A rainbow is a reflection of colored light. You see a rainbow when sunlight shines through raindrops.

When you look at a rainbow, you are seeing a different rainbow from the person who is standing right next to you. The light reflected through the raindrops is seen differently no matter where you stand. No two people see the same rainbow.

Light travels in waves. The light contains different wavelengths. A wavelength is the distance from a point on one wave of light to the same point on another wave of light. Different wavelengths appear as different colors. For example, the longest wavelengths of light appear red. The shortest wavelengths of light appear violet.

The sunlight that you see has many different wavelengths. When all the colors of all the wavelengths mix together, they make white light. That is why the sunshine rays do not appear red or blue.

But when sunlight shines through raindrops, the raindrops act like a prism. A *prism* is a piece of glass that bends rays of light. When the white light bends with a prism, the light breaks into bands of separate colors. That is what raindrops do to sunlight.

The perfect time to see a rainbow is on a hot summer day when there is a late afternoon thunderstorm. Sometimes the sun will come out again while the rain is still falling. To find a rainbow, stand so the sun is behind you. Look in the direction of your shadow. Scan the sky for a rainbow. If you see two rainbows, the bottom one is the primary rainbow. It will be red on the outside and violet on the inside. There will be many colors in between. You may see a second rainbow above this one. That will be the secondary rainbow. It will be violet on the outside and red on the inside. There will be a dark area between these two colors. That is called *Alexander's dark band*.

You can sometimes see rainbows when sunlight hits the water spraying from lawn sprinklers and garden hoses.

Try this:
* Go outside after an afternoon thunderstorm. Try to find a rainbow.
* Try to make a rainbow using a hose or sprinkler.

Leaf Rubbings

Create colorful designs from the leaves and plants you find.

You'll need:

crayons
tissue paper
leaves
newspapers
masking tape
construction paper

1. Place a stack of newspapers on the table.

2. Arrange the leaves on top of the newspaper.

3. Place the tissue paper over the leaves. Tape the edges of the tissue paper to the newspaper.

4. Rub the side of a crayon over the tissue paper.

5. When you are finished rubbing the leaves, mount the tissue paper onto a piece of construction paper, leaving an edge on all sides to make a frame.

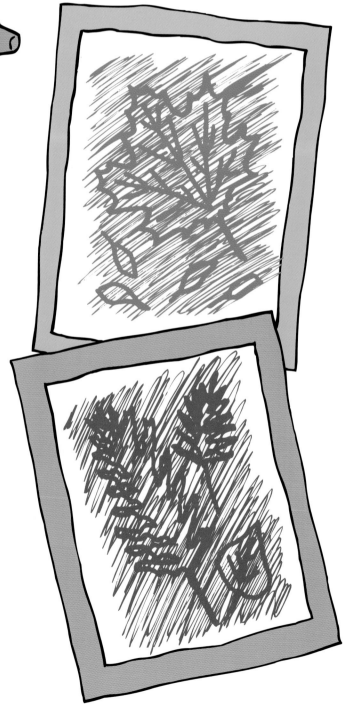

In-Town Rubbings

You can find all kinds of interesting designs in the city.

You'll need:
tracing or typing paper
crayons
construction paper
glue or tape

1. Walk around your town or city. Look for interesting designs and textures like cement blocks, plaques, bricks, carvings, and other things.

2. Lay the paper on top of a design you like. Hold the paper down with one hand while you rub a crayon on its side back and forth on the paper.

3. Glue or tape the design to construction paper to save it.

4. Write on the back what you rubbed to make the design.

Outdoor Weaves

This is a great idea for showing off your nature collections.

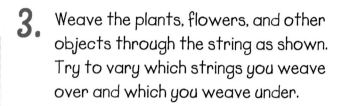

You'll need:
string or yarn
nails
hammer
wooden board
grass, weeds, plants, dried flowers, and
other items you found outside

3. Weave the plants, flowers, and other objects through the string as shown. Try to vary which strings you weave over and which you weave under.

4. STOP When the board is full, ask a grown-up to help you hang it on a wall.

1. STOP Ask a grown-up to hammer a row of nails on each end of the board.

2. Tie one end of the string or yarn to the first nail on either side of the board. Pull the string to the other side of the board and wrap it around the first two nails on that side, as shown. Then pull it back to the other side of the board and wrap it around the next two nails. Continue doing this until you come to the last nail. Tie the end of the string tightly around that nail.

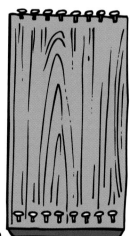

Sunlight Photography

The sun can help you make easy works of art!

You'll need:

dark-colored construction paper
objects from nature like flowers,
   grasses, stones, etc.

1. Find a very bright, sunny spot where the sun feels very strong. Lay a piece of paper on the ground or on a table in that spot.

2. Arrange the flowers, stones, and other items on the paper to make a design.

3. Leave the paper in the sun for at least an hour.

4. Lift the nature items from the paper. What do you see?

Sunshine Silhouettes

A silhouette is a picture of the shape of something.

You'll need:

large sheet of
    white paper
pencil
scissors
black construction
    paper
glue
black crayon

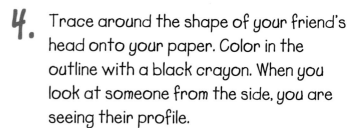

1. Gather your materials. Go outside on a bright, sunny day with a friend.

2. Ask a friend to stand so the sun is behind one side of her as shown.

3. Place your white paper so that the shadow of your friend's head falls onto the paper.

4. Trace around the shape of your friend's head onto your paper. Color in the outline with a black crayon. When you look at someone from the side, you are seeing their profile.

5. **STOP** Ask a grown-up to help you cut out the shape from the paper. Glue it to the black background.

6. Now have your friend trace your silhouette.

Put on those shades and grab the sun-block! The sunniest place in the world is Yuma, Arizona. The yearly average of sunshine is 91 percent of daylight hours. That means about 4,055 hours of sun out of 4,456 possible hours.

The Great Indoors

Sometimes you just can't go outdoors. It might be too cold, or maybe it's raining. That's when it's nice to have a little bit of nature inside. You can decorate your room with art creations made from natural objects. Collect shells, leaves, flowers, bark, or other unusual items on your nature walks. Store them for a rainy-day project. Growing pretty plants inside is another easy way to bring the outside indoors. You can grow fruits and veggies, or just plant pretty flowers to brighten gray, rainy days.

Hearth Cones

Place these pinecones by the fireplace. You'll be ready for a cozy fire when the weather turns cool.

You'll need:

large pinecones
2 pails (1 each for Borax® and salt)
2 wooden spoons (1 each for Borax® and salt)
rubber gloves
2 old pillowcases
newspapers
mesh or paper bags
ribbon
1 pound salt (makes yellow flames)
1 pound Borax® (makes green flames)
2 gallons water

1. Put on the gloves. Spread newspapers all around your work area. Pour the salt into one wooden pail. Pour the Borax® in the other. (🛑 Never mix salt and Borax® together.) Add one gallon of water to each pail. Stir each pail well with a wooden spoon (a different one for each pail).

2. Place a few pinecones in the pillowcase. Dip the pillowcase into one of the pails until it is completely wet. Use one pillowcase for the Borax® bucket and one for the salt bucket. Do not mix them up.

3. Remove the pillowcase from the bucket. Carefully remove the pinecones from the pillowcase. Place them on newspapers to dry completely. This may take three or four days. Continue dipping all your pinecones, using the Borax® bucket for some and the salt bucket for the rest.

4. Hearth cones make terrific Christmas presents! If you want to give your pinecones as gifts, place them in a mesh or paper bag. Tie the bag closed with ribbon. To burn the pinecones, just toss them on top of a fire.

Sand Planter

These colorful planters are a pretty way to display mini plants.

You'll need:
sand
food coloring
large, clean pickle jar
small paper or plastic bowls
tin can with both ends removed
spoon
charcoal
soil
mini houseplants

4. Drop a few small pieces of charcoal into the can. Fill the can with soil. Plant the houseplant. Keep your plant well-watered.

1. Place some sand in each of several paper or plastic bowls. Add food coloring to each to make the colors you want. Mix the sand well until the color is blended into the sand.

2. Pour colored sand into the glass jar until it is almost full. Layer the colors to make a pretty pattern.

3. Carefully push the tin can into the sand. The top of the can should be below the top layer of sand. With the spoon, scoop out any sand that gets inside the can.

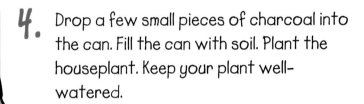

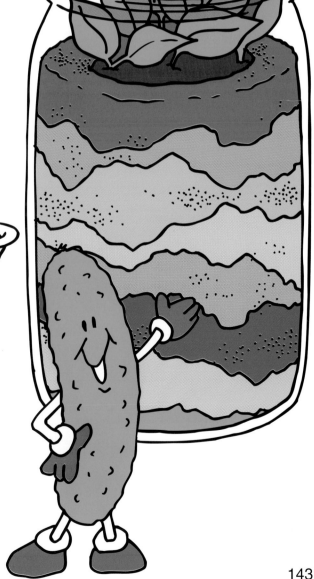

143

Sprout Sponges

Grow sprouts for salads and sandwiches right inside your house!

You'll need:

round, natural sponge
parsley or mustard seeds
string
spray bottle

5. Spray the sponge with water every day.

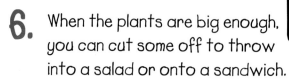

6. When the plants are big enough, you can cut some off to throw into a salad or onto a sandwich.

1. Fill a bucket or bowl with water. Soak the sponge for ten minutes.

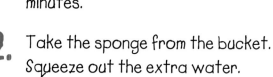

2. Take the sponge from the bucket. Squeeze out the extra water.

3. Place seeds in some of the sponge's holes.

4. Tie the string around the sponge. **STOP** Ask a grown-up to help you hang the sponge where it will get lots of sunlight.

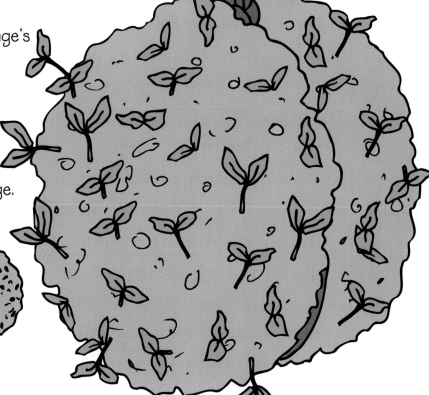

Teeny Weeny Greeny House

An indoor greenhouse is the perfect place to start delicate plants or plants that you want to sprout quickly.

You'll need:

shallow pan
clear lid or cover for the pan
thin peat topsoil briquettes
seeds
flowerpots
stones
potting soil

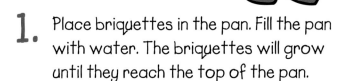

1. Place briquettes in the pan. Fill the pan with water. The briquettes will grow until they reach the top of the pan.

2. Place one or more seeds on each briquette.

3. Place the lid on the pan. Set the greenhouse in a sunny spot.

4. Touch the soil every day. If it feels dry, water the plants.

5. When the sprouts touch the lid, it is time to transplant the seedlings. Put a few pebbles over the hole in each flowerpot. Fill the pots with moist potting soil. Dig a hole in the soil in each pot. Place one plant, along with its briquette, into each pot. Fill in the area around the plants with soil. Place the pots in a sunny place and water when the soil feels dry.

Lovely Lemon and Orange Plants

*You may not be able to grow fruit in your house,
but citrus plants are pretty to look at.*

You'll need:

fresh seeds from
    oranges and lemons
soil
flowerpot

6. If you plant your seeds around December they should sprout in early spring. Seeds planted in spring will sprout in 14 to 30 days. You may see flowers during the summer.

1. Eat an orange or make lemonade. Save the seeds.

2. Fill the flowerpot with moist soil.

3. Push the seeds down about an inch into the soil.

4. Set the pot in a warm, sunny spot. Keep the soil moist at all times.

5. Citrus plants need lots of light, heat, and water. You may also use fertilizer sticks if you want the plants to grow big.

How much do you think a lemon usually weighs? In 1983, the Knutzens in California grew a lemon that weighed 8 pounds 8 ounces! The next time you're at the grocery store, weigh a lemon and see how it measures up!

Awesome Avocado Plant

These plants will grow fruit only if they are grown in a greenhouse, but the plant itself is very pretty.

You'll need:

1 avocado
potted plant
knife
flowerpot
potting soil

1. 🛑 Ask a grown-up to cut the avocado in half. Inside will be a large stone, which is the seed of the plant.

2. Push the stone into the soil of the already-potted plant. Avocados like company when they are sprouting! Water the plants regularly to keep the stone from drying out.

3. Avocado plants take a long time to sprout, so be patient. When you see a couple of leaves sprout from the stone, it's time to transplant.

4. Fill a flowerpot with moist potting soil. Make a well in the middle with your hand. Carefully dig up the avocado plant. Place it in the well in the flowerpot. Cover the roots and stone with soil.

5. Avocado plants need light, but don't let yours sit in direct sunlight. Be sure to water the plant when the soil is dry.

Mexico grows more avocados than any other country. Avocados were originally grown in the West Indies and Central America. (Scientists have found avocado seeds in Mexico that are thousands of years old!)

Avocados are also called avocado pears because of their shape, and alligator pears because of their rough skin. They contain more protein than any other fruit, so they are very nutritious, but they are 25 percent fat!

Nature Notes: Herbs

Herbs are wonderful plants to grow inside if you have a sunny windowsill. You can use them when you cook to add wonderful flavors to your foods. Popular herbs include basil, chives, dill, mint, mustard, parsley, rosemary, sage, and thyme.

Herbs have been used for many things for a long, long time. Scientists have found wild marjoram pollen in caves that date back 60,000 years!

Herbs have sweet or spicy smells. People thought the plants were special because of the way they smelled.

There is written proof that herbs were used around 3000 B.C. But the ancient Romans and Greeks were the first people to write quite a bit about herbs and what they were doing with them.

Mostly, they were using them to cover up bad smells! In those days, they didn't have refrigerators to keep their food cool. The food would start to go bad very quickly. When they served food that wasn't very fresh, they would use a lot of herbs to cover up the bad smell!

DILL   SAGE   THYME   LAVENDER   ROSEMARY

They also didn't bathe very often because it was hard to get water. So herbs were made into oils and perfumes to cover up smelly people! They also scattered herbs on floors and other places to cover up less-than-clean surfaces.

The Greeks and Romans also used herbs to please their gods. They believed the gods had given them herbs to help them cure sickness. To please the gods, they would burn herbs so that the sweet smells would float up to the heavens.

The Greeks and Romans began experimenting with herbs. They believed herbs could be used as medicine, for magic, and for religious reasons. As the Romans went on to conquer many lands, they took their ideas about herbs with them. They spread their herb knowledge to many people. People began growing and selling herbs as a business. Today, we still buy herbs to use in cooking and in decorating.

Try this:
* Plant some herbs in your house. Plant the seeds in small clay flowerpots and place them on a windowsill. Try adding the herbs you grow to some of your favorite foods.
* Dry some herbs and use them to decorate your house. Try making herbal wreaths or potpourri. (Potpourri is a mixture of dried herbs and flowers that gives off a pleasant smell.)

Parsley Planters

Grow fresh parsley to use when you cook.

You'll need:
egg carton
broken eggshells
sponge
parsley seeds
water
scissors

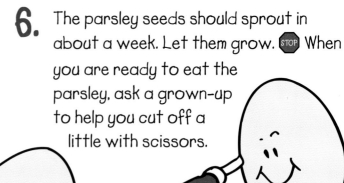

6. The parsley seeds should sprout in about a week. Let them grow. (STOP) When you are ready to eat the parsley, ask a grown-up to help you cut off a little with scissors.

1. Put half an eggshell in each section of the egg carton.

2. (STOP) Ask a grown-up to cut the sponge up into small pieces that will fit inside the eggshells.

3. Hold the sponge pieces under running water. Lightly wring them out. Put a small piece of sponge into each shell.

4. Sprinkle the seeds onto the sponges.

5. Give the seeds a little water each day.

Tip: You can also use parsley as a garnish. A garnish is a decoration placed on a plate of food to make it look pretty.

Hearty Hazelnut Bush

Try to grow your own hazelnuts!

You'll need:

2 whole hazelnuts
flowerpot
soil

1. Start your hazelnut bush in October. Fill the flowerpot with soil. Push the hazelnuts down into the soil. Be sure the nuts are covered by the soil.

2. Find a cool spot in the house. Let the pot sit through the winter. Water the soil only when it looks and feels dry.

3. In the spring, if you want to grow nuts, transplant the bush as you learned in the How Does Your Garden Grow chapter. Or, if you would just like a pretty bush to decorate the house, move the flowerpot to a sunny, warm spot by a window. Trim the bush once in a while to make it fuller.

Marvelous Mango Plant

This beautiful red plant is a pretty sight in any home.

You'll need:
one or more seeds from
    a mango
scrub brush
garden clippers or nail clipper
scissors
soil
flowerpot or
    clean, empty peanut
    butter jar

5. Place the pot in a warm and sunny spot. Water the plant when the soil starts to feel dry. Your plant should sprout in about three weeks. You won't be able to grow any fruit on the plant, but the lovely color of the leaves will add some pizzazz to any room in your house!

1. The outer covering of the seed is called the husk. Scrub each husk with the brush. Try to scrub off any of the orange fruit that is stuck to the seeds. Let the seeds dry overnight.

2. 🛑 Ask a grown-up to clip off the tips of the husks. Then ask your helper to carefully cut the husks open.

3. Take out the big beige seed you find inside each husk. Soak the seeds in water overnight.

4. Pour some soil into the flowerpot or jar. Lay the seeds flat on the soil. Cover the seeds with 1/2 inch of soil.

Tropical Pineapple Plant

Don't throw away that pineapple top! Grow a pineapple plant and pretend you live on a tropical island!

You'll need:

a whole fresh pineapple
large peanut butter jar
   or flowerpot
soil

1. 🛑 Ask a grown-up to cut off the leafy part of the pineapple.

2. With help, remove all the fruit from under the leafy part. If you leave any on the bottom, it will get moldy.

3. Peel off the short leaves at the bottom until you have a two-inch stem.

4. Let the pineapple top sit out and dry for two days.

5. Pour soil into the flowerpot until it is two-thirds full. Place the pineapple top in the soil, so the green tops are pointing up. Push the top into the soil so the soil reaches just to the bottoms of the leaves.

6. Place the flowerpot in a shady spot. Be sure to water the plant enough to keep the soil damp.

7. In about two weeks, you will see new green leaves growing from the pineapple top. When you do, move the pot to a sunny place. Keep watering the plant to keep the soil damp. You probably won't grow any fruit, but the plant itself is very unique-looking.

Pineapples were probably originally grown in Brazil. They may have gotten their name because they look like oversized pinecones.

Pineapple plants grow only in warm places. Thailand grows more pineapples than any other country. Most of the pineapples that are grown in the United States grow in Hawaii.

From the time a pineapple plant is planted, it takes about a year and eight months before the fruit is ready to be picked. Pineapple plants only bear one or two fruits each per harvest.

Personal Peanut Plant

Peanuts can be boiled or roasted, salted or flavored. Use the unroasted kind to grow your own goobers.*

You'll need:

5 fresh, unroasted peanuts, shelled
container that is at least 6 inches
    by 4 inches (best if it is clear plastic)
soil

1. Pour the soil into the container until it is two-thirds full.

2. Place the peanuts on top of the soil. If you have a clear container, you may want to place them near the side of the container. You will be able to watch them grow.

3. Pour about an inch of soil on top of the peanuts. Water the soil until it is damp.

4. Find a warm, sunny place for the container. Be sure to keep the soil damp.

5. In two weeks you will see the first leaves. Let the plants grow until the tallest one is five inches high. Carefully remove the other plants from the container. Throw them out. (You can try to replant the plants you pull out, but they may not grow.)

6. The plant should grow to be about a foot tall. It will have yellow flowers. These yellow flowers will fall off. Smaller flowers will then grow. Little fruits will grow from each of these smaller flowers. They will start bending down toward the soil. They will push into the soil. Peanuts will form under the soil.

7. When the leaves begin to turn yellow, you can dig up the peanuts.

*Peanuts are called many things—ground nuts, pinda, goobers, and ground peas, among other names. The African name for the peanut was nguba, which is where the word goober came from.

A peanut is not a nut. It's a kind of pea. Peanuts were first grown by the Mayan Indians. Scientists have found jars with peanut designs in Peruvian tombs that are more than 1,500 years old!

How big are the peanuts you grow? In 1990 a 4-inch-long peanut was grown in Enfield, North Carolina. But most peanuts are about half that size.

Glossary

annual A plant that lives for only a year.

bark A thick layer around the trunk and branches of a tree that protects the tree.

bud A small, new shoot on a plant that holds the new leaves of the plant.

bulb A stem of a plant that is planted underground.

chlorophyll The green pigment found in plants. It gives plants their green color and helps them make food.

constellation Stars that are grouped together and form patterns.

cultivation Preparing land to grow crops.

environment The world in which a specific living thing lives. Your environment includes your home, your school, and your neighborhood.

fossils Impressions or parts of plants and animals that lived long ago.

fruit The part of the plant that holds the seed.

harvest To pick the full-grown fruit or vegetables from a plant.

Glossary

herbs Plants with nice smells that are used to add flavor to food.

humidity The amount of water in air.

migrate When a living thing moves a long way to a new home at the same time each year.

perennial A plant that lives year after year.

photosynthesis When plants use carbon dioxide, light, water, and chlorophyll to make food.

ripe When a fruit or vegetable is fully grown and is ready to eat.

root The part of the plant that is underground. It holds the plant to the ground and absorbs water and nutrients from the soil.

seed The part of the plant found in the fruit. If you plant the seed, new plants will grow.

seedling A small, new plant that has grown from a seed.

transplant To move from one place to another.

INDEX

INDEX

INDEX

INDEX